NORTH CAROLINA TEST PREP

Ultimate Practice Test Book

End-of-Grade Reading

Grade 3

ISBN 9798521451951

CONTENTS

INTRODUCTION
For Parents, Teachers, and Tutors

About North Carolina's Reading Assessments

Students in North Carolina will be assessed each year by taking the End-of-Grade Reading assessments. On these tests, students read a range of literary and informational passages and answer around 50 multiple choice questions about the passages.

This practice test book will prepare students for the test. It contains four complete practice tests that cover all the skills assessed and give students experience with all the passage and question types found on the test.

About North Carolina's English Language Arts Standards

Student learning and assessment in North Carolina is based on the skills listed in the *North Carolina Standard Course of Study*. These standards were introduced in 2017 and fully implemented in the 2018-2019 school year. The reading standards are divided into two areas: Reading Standards for Literature and Reading Standards for Informational Text. This practice test book covers all the reading skills assessed on the test.

Developing Advanced Reading Skills

The state tests require students to read literary and informational passages and answer questions to show understanding of the texts. This practice test book contains rigorous questions that require students to read texts closely, to provide supporting evidence, and to evaluate and synthesize texts. These advanced questions will encourage a deep understanding of texts and help students excel on the End-of-Grade tests. While the actual test only contains multiple choice questions, these additional practice questions will give students the skills to understand, analyze, and respond to a wide range of complex texts.

Taking the Test

Each practice test in this book contains about 72 questions. This is longer than the actual End-of-Grade test, which has around 50 questions. The additional length ensures that all skills are tested and a wide range of passages and question types are included. Each practice test is divided into two sessions. Students should be able to complete each session in 90 minutes.

End-of-Grade Reading

Practice Test 1

Session 1

Instructions

Read each passage and answer the questions that follow it.

For each multiple-choice question, fill in the circle for the correct answer. For other types of questions, follow the instructions given. Some of the questions require a written answer. Write your answer on the lines provided.

A Campfire Story

The Baxter twins, Erik and Kirsty, could not wait for summer vacation. They were finally old enough to go to Camp Arrowhead in northern Canada. The camp rules stated you had to have completed fourth grade to attend the overnight camp. There would be horseback riding, canoeing, nature hikes, swimming in the lake, cookouts, campfires, and even a softball tournament.

Mother and Father packed the kids up and headed north. It was a four-hour drive. The road wound through the mountains and thick-forested land. They stopped for lunch along the way. After driving some more, the kids knew they were almost at the camp.

"There's the sign!" Erik screamed, pointing to the wooden camp sign on the edge of the road.

"I can't believe we're finally here! Let's hurry," Kirsty said.

Erik and Kirsty grabbed their backpacks and sleeping bags, and then they gave Mother and Father a hug. "See you Friday!" they said together. They couldn't stop giggling.

"Jinx," Erik and Kirsty looked at each other and laughed.

After registration, it was time to get settled in their cabins and meet the other campers. Erik spotted the boys' cabin up the hill. Kirsty followed the trail to the girls' cabin. They rolled out their sleeping bags. Then they unpacked their clothes.

A shrill whistle sounded. It was time for the swim test. The test was to see which campers would be allowed to swim in the deepest area of the swim zone. They needed to swim 100 yards without stopping. Erik and Kirsty waded in the cool lake water and began their swim. There were lots of other swimmers.

"I'm glad Mom had us take swim lessons," Erik said.

"Same here," Kirsty added. "This is pretty easy."

The waterfront director smiled at the swimmers. "You have all done a great job! During open swim times, you can swim in the entire swimming zone and out to the raft. Great swimming!"

A shrill whistle sounded again. It was time for dinner.

"Yummy! I'll have two hot dogs please, a bag of chips, and a carton of chocolate milk," Erik said to the cook.

"And I will have the same," Kirsty said. "Thank you."

The cook passed out long metal sticks and marshmallows to roast over the campfire. "Be careful with the sticks. Don't poke anyone. When you have roasted your marshmallows, help yourself to crackers and a piece of chocolate. They're over on the picnic table."

"Wow, s'mores! My favorite!" Kirsty said, licking her sticky fingers.

"Who has a story to share?" the camp director asked. The counselors shared their stories first. Some stories were funny and some were a little scary. Then a few campers shared their stories. Kirsty just sat by Erik and enjoyed the warm fire.

"I can't think of any story to tell," Kirsty whispered to Erik.

"Well, that's okay. Maybe tomorrow you will have a story to share," Erik said.

"Time for bed," the camp director told the campers. "We have a full day of activities planned for tomorrow. Glad to see all of you at camp this week. Have a nice sleep. And don't go dreaming of any ghosts!"

The campers smiled.

"Good night, Erik," Kirsty said. "See you bright and early."

"Yeah, thanks," Erik replied. "I'll save a spot in the dining hall for you at breakfast."

Kirsty snuggled into her sleeping bag and quickly fell asleep. She was very tired from the long trip and the swim test. And it was late – past 10 o'clock. She usually went to bed much earlier.

In the middle of the night, Kirsty felt something soft and furry touch her hand. She sat up in bed. The room was dark. She was just about to scream. Then she quickly covered her mouth and stopped herself. Whatever this was, she did not want to frighten it.

Just as she turned her flashlight on, a small black animal with a striped tail jumped off her sleeping bag and scooted under her bed.

"That looked like a skunk," she said to herself. "Hmm, I hope it's not frightened. I wouldn't want it to smell up the cabin."

Then she had an idea. She tiptoed over to the window and opened it. Then she walked quietly over to the far corner of the room and squatted down. She turned off the flashlight.

In a few minutes, Kirsty heard a loud noise. There was scampering across the wooden floor and then no more noise. She waited. There was only silence. She counted to ten just in case.

And then Kirsty turned on the flashlight and slowly crept over to her bed. She shone the light under the bed and all around her sleeping bag. There was no skunk to be found. It was a relief. She shut the window and jumped back into bed.

Tomorrow she would have a story to tell around the campfire.

1   What does the photograph at the start of the passage help the reader understand?

    Ⓐ   the characters

    Ⓑ   the theme

    Ⓒ   the plot

    Ⓓ   the setting

2   According to the passage, why were Erik and Kirsty unable to go to the camp earlier?

    Ⓐ   They were not old enough.

    Ⓑ   They could not swim well enough.

    Ⓒ   They lived too far away.

    Ⓓ   They had not saved enough money.

3   How do Erik and Kirsty feel when they first arrive at the camp?

    Ⓐ   disappointed

    Ⓑ   excited

    Ⓒ   nervous

    Ⓓ   tired

4   Why are Kirsty and Erik able to complete the swimming test easily?

    Ⓐ   They live near the sea and swim all the time.

    Ⓑ   They took swimming lessons.

    Ⓒ   They help each other.

    Ⓓ   They really want to swim in the deepest part.

5   Which dialogue suggests an event that is going to happen next that is important to the storyline?

    Ⓐ   *"I can't believe we're finally here! Let's hurry," Kirsty said.*

    Ⓑ   *"You have all done a great job! During open swim times, you can swim in the entire swimming zone and out to the raft. Great swimming!"*

    Ⓒ   *"Well, that's okay. Maybe tomorrow you will have a story to share," Erik said.*

    Ⓓ   *"Yeah, thanks," Erik replied. "I'll save a spot in the dining hall for you at breakfast."*

6   Circle the word from the paragraph below that suggests that Kirsty was warm and comfortable.

Kirsty snuggled into her sleeping bag and quickly fell asleep. She was very tired from the long trip and the swim test. And it was late – past 10 o'clock. She usually went to bed much earlier.

7   How does Kirsty feel when she first feels the skunk touch her hand?

    Ⓐ   calm

    Ⓑ   confused

    Ⓒ   embarrassed

    Ⓓ   frightened

8   Which sentence from the passage best supports your answer to Question 7?

    Ⓐ   *She sat up in bed.*

    Ⓑ   *The room was dark.*

    Ⓒ   *She was just about to scream.*

    Ⓓ   *Then she quickly covered her mouth and stopped herself.*

9   What is Kirsty afraid of the skunk doing?

    Ⓐ   waking up the other campers

    Ⓑ   scratching or biting her

    Ⓒ   making the cabin smell bad

    Ⓓ   creating a mess

10   Place the events that occur in the passage in order from first to last. Write the numbers 1, 2, 3, and 4 on the lines to show the order.

_____   Kirsty listens to people tell stories.

_____   Kirsty completes a swimming test.

_____   Kirsty finds her cabin and unpacks.

_____   Kirsty makes s'mores.

11   How does Kirsty get the skunk to leave her cabin? Use **two** details from the passage in your answer.

_____

_____

_____

_____

12   Is the way Kirsty reacts to the skunk smart? Explain why you feel that way.

_____

_____

_____

_____

Endangered Animals Matter

Animals are becoming endangered faster than ever before. Endangered animals are at risk of becoming extinct. Extinct animals are gone forever. Lots of people know about the big animals that are endangered. Orangutans, Javan rhinos and the lowland gorilla are all endangered. People care when big animals become endangered. You might have heard about some in the United States. The grey wolf, the Florida panther, and the cougar are endangered American animals. But what about insects? Do people care when insects become endangered? Some insects bite, or get in our food. Wouldn't they be good to get rid of?

The Rusty Patched Bumblebee

One very important insect has just become endangered. The rusty patched bumblebee is the very first endangered American bee. The bumblebee is dark brown with light brown patches on top. It used to be in lots of gardens, but now it has almost disappeared. There are 4,000 native species of bees in the United States. Only 40 of the bee species are bumblebees.

But do we really need bees? They sting! Actually, bees are really important. Bees, wasps, and ants are some of the most important insects in the whole world! Bees go from flower to flower collecting pollen. They take the pollen from one plant to another. This is called pollination. Plants need pollination. If we didn't have bees, many plants would not be pollinated and would not make seeds. Other animals, like butterflies, pollinate plants too. If we didn't have insects to carry pollen from flower to flower we would have no wild flowers. Imagine a world without flowers! And don't forget about honey and beeswax! These important products are only produced by bees.

There are other endangered insects in the United States as well. Blue butterflies, emerald dragonflies, and tiger beetles are some of them.

Ohlone Tiger Beetles

Tiger beetles are colorful beetles that live in California. They kill insects that eat our food. Tiger beetles need bare ground to live on. This is the beetles' habitat. More and more people are building houses in California. The beetles' habitat is getting smaller and smaller. People ride bikes through their habitat and squash them, or accidentally spread grass on the bare ground. The biggest reason why animals become endangered is because they lose their habitat.

Bug-eating Bats

Bats are bug-eaters too. They eat the bugs that eat our crops and trees. If we didn't have bats, our crops and trees would be in trouble. Bats in the United States are becoming endangered. A disease called white-nose syndrome is making them sick. White-nose is the worst wildlife disease that we have ever had. It gives them a fuzzy white nose and wings. They get very sick and often die. Seven species of bat are sick so far. If we don't help them, they might become extinct. Little brown bats are almost all gone. Scientists are trying to work out what to do. They might be able to make a medicine for the bats.

The bats' habitat is also being taken. Trees are being cut down and people are working in their habitat. Chemicals in the environment are also damaging the bats.

What Can We Do?

We need lots of different animals on our planet. A wide variety of animals is beautiful. It is also important. Animals all have different jobs to do. Even the animals we don't like! They help with the air, water, food, and medicines. They help us live. Animals becoming endangered is a serious problem. We need to find solutions. There are three main solutions.

The first one is science. Scientists learn about the animals and find out how to help them. Scientists are trying to make medicine for the bats. They are also finding out about insects and how to protect them.

The second solution is law. Laws that protect the animals are needed. Some laws protect habitats. Some laws stop people catching animals.

The last solution is education. If people know why animals are important they will protect them. Photos and videos of the animals show people what they do. Wildlife reserves and zoos teach people about endangered animals too.

Stand Up for the Animals

Be an animal protector. Join a group that helps animals. It could be a major international group like the World Wide Fund for Nature (WFF), a small group that focuses on one animal, or a local group in your area. Your support will help protect animal habitats.

The animals need us to protect them and we need them to live. All endangered animals need our help. This includes the big ones and the tiny ones!

Solutions at Home

You can even do some things at home to protect our wildlife.

Bringing your cats in at night protects birds. Every year, lots of birds are killed by cats or by hitting windows. Putting decals on your windows helps too.

Make sure animals can't eat your garbage. Eating garbage can kill an animal.

Plant native plants in your garden to feed native bees and butterflies. Use safe bug sprays on your garden too. Chemical sprays can kill wildlife.

13   Use details from the passage to complete the web with **four** more examples of large endangered animals.

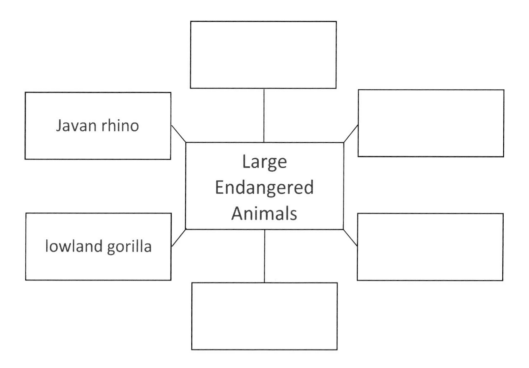

14   Which sentence below compares and contrasts?

Ⓐ   *One very important insect has just become endangered.*

Ⓑ   *The bumblebee is dark brown with light brown patches on top.*

Ⓒ   *It used to be in lots of gardens, but now it has almost disappeared.*

Ⓓ   *There are 4,000 native species of bees in the United States.*

15   Which question is answered in the section titled "The Rusty Patched Bumblebee"?

ⓐ   Why has the rusty patched bumblebee become endangered?

ⓑ   What can people do to help the rusty patched bumblebee?

ⓒ   How has the number of rusty patched bumblebees changed?

ⓓ   Does the rusty patched bumblebee sting people?

16   Read this sentence from the passage.

Tiger beetles need bare ground to live on.

What does the word <u>bare</u> mean?

ⓐ   covered

ⓑ   empty

ⓒ   safe

ⓓ   warm

17   Based on the passage, which solution listed is most likely to help endangered bats?

ⓐ   education

ⓑ   law

ⓒ   science

ⓓ   wildlife groups

18   What is the main purpose of the section titled "Stand Up for the Animals"?

Ⓐ   to show the important work that people do to help animals

Ⓑ   to tell how animals have become endangered

Ⓒ   to explain why it is important to take action

Ⓓ   to encourage people to join a group that helps save animals

19   What is the main message of the section titled "Solutions at Home"?

Ⓐ   There are too many animals that need help.

Ⓑ   Small animals are often overlooked.

Ⓒ   Everyone can play a part in helping animals.

Ⓓ   All animals need to live together.

20   Complete the web below by listing **three** things that people wouldn't have if bees did not pollinate plants.

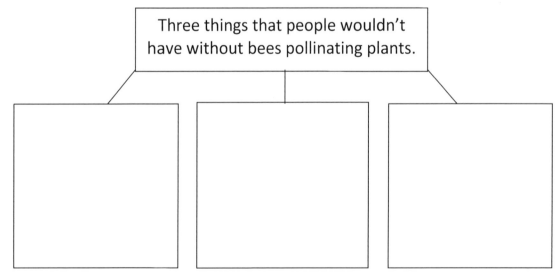

Three things that people wouldn't have without bees pollinating plants.

21   Describe **two** actions that people take that harm Ohlone tiger beetles.

    1: _____

    _____

    2: _____

    _____

22   What is the difference between an endangered animal and an extinct animal? Use **two** details from the passage in your answer.

    _____

    _____

    _____

    _____

    _____

23 In the third paragraph, the author asks if people really need bees. What would the author's answer be? Use **two** details from the passage to support your answer.

_____

_____

_____

_____

_____

_____

24 Which solution in the section titled "Solutions at Home" would most help bees?

Ⓐ   bringing cats in at night

Ⓑ   putting decals on windows

Ⓒ   keeping garbage out of reach

Ⓓ   planting native plants

The Nettle

Anna (*jumping up and down*): Oh, papa! I have stung my hand with that nettle.

Father: Well, my dear, I am sorry for it. But pull up that large dock leaf you see near it. Now bruise the juice out of it on the part which is stung. Well, is the pain lessened?

Anna: Oh, very much indeed, I hardly feel it now. But I wish there was not a nettle in the world. I am sure I do not know what use there can be in them.

Father: If you knew anything of botany, you would not say so.

Anna: What is botany, papa?

Father: Botany, my dear, is the knowledge of plants.

Anna: Some plants are very beautiful. If the lily were growing in our fields, I should not complain. But this ugly nettle! I do not know what beauty or use there can be in that.

Father: And yet, there is more beauty, use, and instruction in a nettle, than even in a lily.

Anna: Oh papa, how can you make that out?

Father: Put on your gloves, pluck up that nettle, and let us examine it. First, look at the flower.

Anna: The flower, papa? I see no flower, unless those little ragged knobs are flowers, which have neither color nor smell, and are not much larger than the heads of pins.

Father: Here, take this magnifying glass and examine them.

Anna: Oh, I see now. Every little knob is folded up in leaves, like a rosebud. Perhaps there is a flower inside.

Father: Take this pin and touch the knob.

Anna: Oh, how curious!

Father: What is curious?

Anna: The moment I touched it, it flew open. A little cloud rose out like enchantment, and four beautiful little stems sprung up as if they were alive. And, now that I look again with the glass, I see an elegant little flower as nice and perfect as a lily itself.

Father: Well, now examine the leaves.

Anna: Oh, I see they are all covered over with little bristles. And when I examine them with the glass, I see a little bag, filled with a juice like water, at the bottom of each. Ha! These are the things which stung me.

Father: Now touch the little bag with the point of the pin.

Anna: When I press the bag, the juice runs up and comes out at the small point at the top. So I suppose the little thorn must be hollow inside, though it is finer than the point of my needle.

Father: Have all the leaves those stings?

Anna: No, papa. Some of the young ones are quite green and soft, like velvet, and I may handle them without any danger.

Father: Now look at the stem, and break it.

Anna: I can easily crack it, but I cannot break it, for the bark is so strong that it holds it together.

Father: Well, now you see there are more curious things in the nettle than you expected.

Anna: Yes, indeed, I see that. But I am sure I cannot see any use in all these things.

Father: That we will now consider. You saw the little flower burst open, and a cloud rose, you say, like enchantment. Now all this is necessary for the nature of the plant. Now look at this other nettle, which grew on the opposite side of the road. You see that it is not exactly like the one you have just examined.

Anna: No, papa. This one has little flat seeds instead of flowers.

Father: Very right, my dear. Now, in order to make those seeds grow, it is necessary that the little flower of this plant and the seed of that should be together, as they are in most others. But plants cannot walk, like animals. Nature has provided a remedy for this. When the little flower bursts open it throws out a fine powder, which you saw rise like a cloud. This is conveyed by the air to the other plant, and when it falls upon the seed of that plant it gives it power to grow. This makes it a perfect seed, which, in its turn, when it falls to the ground, will produce a new plant. Were it not for this fine powder, that seed would never be perfect or complete.

Anna: That is very curious, indeed. And I see the use of the little cloud and the flower. But the leaf that stung me, of what use can that be?

Father: Even these stings are made useful. The people in some countries use them when they are sick. Those leaves which do not sting are used by some for food, and from the stalk others get a stringy bark. This bark is used to make linen, and that linen can be used to make clothing. Even nettle leaves that sting can be used to make a healthy tea. Thus you see that even the despised nettle is not made in vain.

25   In the first line of the play, why is Anna jumping up and down?

  Ⓐ   She is angry.

  Ⓑ   She is in pain.

  Ⓒ   She is excited.

  Ⓓ   She is frightened.

26   Read this line from the play.

> **Father: Well, my dear, I am sorry for it. But pull up that large dock leaf you see near it. Now bruise the juice out of it on the part which is stung. Well, is the pain lessened?**

As it is used in the line, what does <u>lessened</u> mean?

  Ⓐ   aching

  Ⓑ   increased

  Ⓒ   reduced

  Ⓓ   understood

27   According to Anna, why is the lily better than the nettle?

  Ⓐ   It has more uses.

  Ⓑ   It is more beautiful.

  Ⓒ   It does not sting.

  Ⓓ   It is easier to grow.

28 Read this line from the play.

> **Father: Put on your gloves, pluck up that nettle, and let us examine it. First, look at the flower.**

What is the most likely reason the father has Anna put on gloves?

Ⓐ   so she does not harm the nettle

Ⓑ   so nobody knows they plucked the nettle

Ⓒ   so she does not get stung by the nettle

Ⓓ   so she can feel the nettle better

29 In which line below is the father giving Anna an instruction?

Ⓐ   *Father: Botany, my dear, is the knowledge of plants.*

Ⓑ   *Father: What is curious?*

Ⓒ   *Father: Now touch the little bag with the point of the pin.*

Ⓓ   *Father: Have all the leaves those stings?*

30 Read this sentence spoken by the father.

> **This is conveyed by the air to the other plant, and when it falls upon the seed of that plant it gives it power to grow.**

As it is used in the sentence, what does <u>conveyed</u> mean?

Ⓐ   carried

Ⓑ   changed

Ⓒ   explained

Ⓓ   lost

31   Which of these best describes what the father is doing throughout the play?

   Ⓐ   comforting Anna

   Ⓑ   warning Anna

   Ⓒ   teaching Anna

   Ⓓ   mocking Anna

32   Which statement best summarizes the theme of the play?

   Ⓐ   Be careful what you wish for.

   Ⓑ   Everything has its purpose.

   Ⓒ   Appreciate what you have.

   Ⓓ   Accept people's differences.

33   Based on your answer to Question 32, which sentence from the play best summarizes the theme?

   Ⓐ   *But I wish there was not a nettle in the world.*

   Ⓑ   *If the lily were growing in our fields, I should not complain.*

   Ⓒ   *You see that it is not exactly like the one you have just examined.*

   Ⓓ   *Thus you see that even the despised nettle is not made in vain.*

34   Circle **two** words from the line below that show that the plant's movement was sudden and quick.

Anna: The moment I touched it, it flew open. A little cloud rose out like enchantment, and four beautiful little stems sprung up as if they were alive. And, now that I look again with the glass, I see an elegant little flower as nice and perfect as a lily itself.

35   Complete the table below by listing **one** purpose of each part of the plant.

Purposes of Nettle

Part of the Plant	Purpose
stings	
leaves	
stalk	

36   How do you think Anna's feelings about nettle change by the end of the play? Use at least **two** details from the play to support your answer.

_____

_____

_____

_____

_____

_____

_____

_____

_____

_____

_____

_____

_____

_____

_____

End-of-Grade Reading

Practice Test 1

Session 2

Instructions

Read each passage and answer the questions that follow it.

For each multiple-choice question, fill in the circle for the correct answer. For other types of questions, follow the instructions given. Some of the questions require a written answer. Write your answer on the lines provided.

How to Start Painting

Where to Begin

If you are interested in learning to paint, there are many things to consider. The first thing you must consider is what style and method of painting you would like to learn! First, you can talk to friends, family, painters, your art teacher, and other people that you know. Ask for their opinion on painting and if they know anyone who paints in their career or as a hobby.

Second, learn more about both oil painting and acrylic painting. Third, find out which one you are more interested in learning. Oil and acrylic painting are both very fun, but are also very different. Some painters enjoy both, but many professional painters choose to become skillful in either oils or acrylics. Lastly, after you make your decision, make a list of the materials you will need!

What You Will Need

Once you decide whether you are interested in learning about painting with oils or acrylics, then you can research what materials you will need and make a list! Think about where you can buy the materials for the best price. You can look online, in specialty art stores, large arts and crafts chains, and local art stores. Regardless of whether you choose to use acrylics or oils, you will need to buy the primary colors. These are red, yellow, and blue. You will also need black and white. With these basic five colors, you can create almost any painting you can imagine!

You will also need paintbrushes. Before you make a decision about what paintbrushes to buy, talk to your art class teacher, a painter, or a local art instructor, to learn more about the different kind of paintbrushes. You can also talk to salespersons in a store. They may have valuable information and insight about buying paintbrushes.

Of course, you can't make a painting without canvas! Although there are many different kinds of canvas, if you are just learning to paint, try buying a few small pieces of student canvas first. You can always try using other canvas types and sizes later.

If you have paints, paintbrushes, and a canvas, you may be ready to paint using acrylics. However, if you choose to try oil painting, you will need quite a few more materials. Oil painters also need paint thinner to wash their brushes, linseed oil to mix with the oil paints, a spatula or paint knife, and a palette.

Whether you choose to start oil painting or acrylic painting, it helps to wear old or messy clothes that you are not worried about ruining. You should also have quick access to paper towels and newspaper for quick clean-up and to prevent your brushes from getting too messy while you are painting.

Ways of Learning

Many beginner painters decide to take a painting class at a local art studio. Others, however, enjoy starting out alone at home. If you are just starting out, consider calling or contacting a local art studio to find out if they offer painting classes. Sometimes art stores also offer painting classes. There are a lot of ways to learn to paint! You can also learn methods for painting from watching videos on the Internet.

Some people learn best from taking a class, others learn best from watching videos, and others just try and work it out themselves. You can choose what is best for you. Many people choose a combination of classes and painting at home alone. If you know someone who paints, ask them if you can spend some time observing them. You can learn more just by watching them!

Start Painting

Every famous or advanced painter was a beginner once! Everybody starts from the beginning. When you get ready to start painting, be certain that you have a positive attitude! If you try to paint but feel bad about your painting, don't worry, because you can always add paint again on top. It's not a problem to stop painting for the day if you are frustrated, and work on the painting again the next day! Actually, if you choose oil painting, you usually have to wait a few days for your painting to dry a little, before painting again on top of the painting. Acrylic paints, however, dry very quickly, and you can paint very easily on top of acrylic paint without seeing the bottom color.

Practice Makes Perfect

Don't forget that practice makes perfect! The more you practice anything, the better you can become! Some people are naturally gifted in painting, but many painters have become famous painters because they had a lot of practice! Some famous painters did not even become famous until after they died. Don't be discouraged if you are not a perfect painter after taking one painting class, or even after a few years of painting. Painting is a skill! People who love to paint, often choose to paint because they love being creative and trying new things. If you are interested in learning how to paint, keep an open mind, use your creativity, and have some patience.

Even if your paintings are not perfect, painting can still be a fun and relaxing hobby.

37 How is the section titled "Where to Begin" mainly organized?

    Ⓐ   cause and effect

    Ⓑ   order of events

    Ⓒ   problem and solution

    Ⓓ   compare and contrast

38 What does the author say is the best way to decide what style and method of painting to learn?

    Ⓐ   research the costs of each style

    Ⓑ   ask different people for advice

    Ⓒ   try each style to see which one you are good at

    Ⓓ   visit a local art store and speak to a salesperson

39 Circle the **five** colors of paints the author states that artists will need to buy.

black	blue	green
orange	pink	purple
red	white	yellow

40   Read this sentence from the passage.

> **They may have valuable information and insight about buying paintbrushes.**

As it is used in the sentence, what does <u>valuable</u> mean?

Ⓐ   costly

Ⓑ   secret

Ⓒ   unique

Ⓓ   useful

41   Complete the web below by listing the **four** items needed for oil painting that are not also needed for acrylic painting.

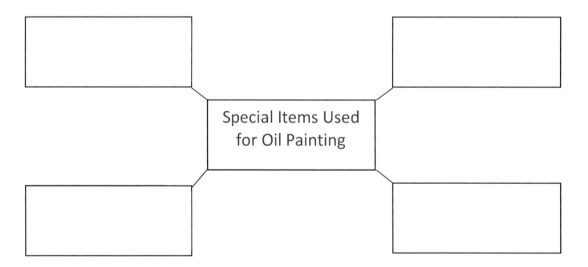

42   What is the main idea of the second paragraph of the section titled "Ways of Learning"?

    Ⓐ   Take learning to paint seriously.

    Ⓑ   Choose what learning method works for you.

    Ⓒ   Be willing to share your work.

    Ⓓ   Paint alone as often as you can.

43   What does the photograph in the section titled "Ways of Learning" most likely represent?

    Ⓐ   painting alone at home

    Ⓑ   watching videos online

    Ⓒ   taking an art class

    Ⓓ   watching someone paint

44   Read these sentences from the passage.

> **Every famous or advanced painter was a beginner once! Everybody starts from the beginning.**

The author most likely includes these sentences to –

    Ⓐ   encourage the reader

    Ⓑ   teach the reader

    Ⓒ   tease the reader

    Ⓓ   warn the reader

45 Read this sentence from the passage.

> **Some people are naturally gifted in painting, but many painters have become famous painters because they had a lot of practice!**

As it is used in the sentence, which word means about the same as <u>gifted</u>?

Ⓐ   creative

Ⓑ   generous

Ⓒ   marvelous

Ⓓ   talented

46 Based on the information in the section titled "Start Painting," list **two** pieces of advice the author gives for when someone might be annoyed or frustrated with his or her work.

1: _____

_____

2: _____

_____

47 Describe **one** main benefit of choosing acrylic painting over oil painting. Use details from the section titled "What You Will Need" to support your answer.

_____

_____

_____

_____

_____

48 How does the photograph at the end of the passage support the statement made in the caption? Explain your answer.

_____

_____

_____

_____

_____

How Brother Rabbit Fooled the Whale and the Elephant

One day Brother Rabbit was running along on the sand. He was going to a fine cabbage field. On the way he saw the whale and the elephant talking together.

Brother Rabbit said, "I'd like to know what they are talking about." So he crouched down behind some bushes and listened.

This is what Brother Rabbit heard the whale say:

"You are the biggest thing on the land, Brother Elephant, and I am the biggest thing in the sea. If we work together, we can rule all the animals in the world. We can have our own way about everything."

"Very good, very good," trumpeted the elephant. "That suits me. You keep the sea, and I will keep the land."

"That's a bargain," said the whale, as he swam away.

Brother Rabbit laughed to himself. "They won't rule me," he said, as he ran off.

Brother Rabbit soon came back with a very long and a very strong rope and his big drum. He hid the drum in some bushes. Then taking one end of the rope, he walked up to the elephant.

"Oh, dear Mr. Elephant," he said, "you are big and strong. Will you have the kindness to do me a favor?"

The elephant was pleased, and he trumpeted, "Certainly, certainly. What is it?"

"My cow is stuck in the mud on the shore, and I can't pull her out," said Brother Rabbit. "If you will help me, you will do me a great service. You are so strong, I am sure you can get her out."

"Certainly, certainly," trumpeted the elephant.

"Thank you," said the rabbit. "Take this rope in your trunk, and I will tie the other end to my cow. Then I will beat my drum to let you know when to pull. You must pull as hard as you can, for the cow is very heavy."

"Huh!" trumpeted the elephant, "I'll pull her out, or break the rope."

Brother Rabbit tied the rope to the elephant's trunk and ran off.

He ran till he came to the shore where the whale was. Making a bow, Brother Rabbit said, "Oh, mighty and wonderful Whale, will you do me a favor?"

"What is it?" asked the whale.

"My cow is stuck in the mud on the shore," said Brother Rabbit, "and I cannot pull her out. Of course you can do it. If you will be so kind as to help me, I shall be very much obliged."

"Certainly," said the whale, "certainly."

"Thank you," said Brother Rabbit, "take hold of this rope, and I will tie the other end to my cow. Then I will beat my big drum to let you know when to pull. You must pull as hard as you can, for my cow is very heavy."

"Never fear," said the whale, "I could pull a dozen cows out of the mud."

"I am sure you could," said the rabbit politely. "Only be sure to begin gently. Then pull harder and harder till you get her out."

The rabbit ran away into the bushes where he had hidden the drum and began to beat it. Then the whale began to pull and the elephant began to pull. In a minute the rope tightened till it was stretched as hard as a bar of iron.

"This is a very heavy cow," said the elephant, "but I'll pull her out." Bracing his fore feet in the earth, he gave a tremendous pull.

But the whale had no way to brace himself.

"Dear me," he said. "That cow must surely be stuck tight." Lashing his tail in the water, he gave a marvelous pull.

He pulled harder; the elephant pulled harder. Soon the whale found himself sliding toward the land. He was so focused on the cow that he went head first, down to the bottom of the sea.

That was a pull! The elephant was jerked off his feet, and came slipping and sliding toward the sea. He was very angry.

"That cow must be very strong to drag me in this way," he said. "I will brace myself."

Kneeling down on the ground, he twisted the rope around his trunk. Then he began to pull his very best, and soon the whale came up out of the water.

Then each saw that the other had hold of the rope.

"How is this?" cried the whale. "I thought I was pulling Brother Rabbit's cow."

"That is what I thought," said the elephant. "Brother Rabbit is making fun of us. He must pay for this. I forbid him to eat a blade of grass on land, because he played a trick on us."

"And I will not allow him to drink a drop of water in the sea," said the whale.

But Little Rabbit sat in the bushes and laughed, and laughed, and laughed.

"Much do I care," he said. "I can get all the green things I want, and I don't like salt water."

49   In the second paragraph, why does the rabbit crouch down behind the bushes?

Ⓐ   He is looking for cabbages.

Ⓑ   He wants to listen in on the elephant and the whale.

Ⓒ   He plans to jump out and scare the elephant.

Ⓓ   He is tired and needs to rest.

50   Which sentence best explains why the rabbit decides to fool the whale and the elephant?

Ⓐ   *On the way he saw the whale and the elephant talking together.*

Ⓑ   *Brother Rabbit laughed to himself.*

Ⓒ   *"They won't rule me," he said, as he ran off.*

Ⓓ   *Brother Rabbit soon came back with a very long and a very strong rope and his big drum.*

51   Read this sentence from the passage.

"Huh!" trumpeted the elephant, "I'll pull her out, or break the rope."

What does this sentence show about the elephant?

Ⓐ   He knows the rabbit is trying to fool him.

Ⓑ   He is worried about embarrassing himself.

Ⓒ   He fears he will hurt the cow.

Ⓓ   He is very confident he is strong enough.

52   Read this sentence spoken by the rabbit.

If you will be so kind as to help me, I shall be very much obliged.

The phrase "very much obliged" means that the rabbit will be –

Ⓐ   annoyed

Ⓑ   grateful

Ⓒ   loyal

Ⓓ   surprised

53   Circle the simile used in the paragraph below.

The rabbit ran away into the bushes where he had hidden the drum and began to beat it. Then the whale began to pull and the elephant began to pull. In a minute the rope tightened till it was stretched as hard as a bar of iron.

54   Which sentence best explains why the drum is important to the rabbit's plan?

Ⓐ   It stops the cow from getting scared.

Ⓑ   It makes the scene funny.

Ⓒ   It tells the whale and the elephant to pull at the same time.

Ⓓ   It keeps other animals away from the area.

55 Which of these phrases from the passage creates a humorous image?

Ⓐ   *Bracing his fore feet in the earth*

Ⓑ   *Lashing his tail in the water*

Ⓒ   *slipping and sliding toward the sea*

Ⓓ   *twisted the rope around his trunk*

56 What type of passage is "How Brother Rabbit Fooled the Whale and the Elephant"?

Ⓐ   fable

Ⓑ   mystery

Ⓒ   historical fiction

Ⓓ   science fiction

57 The main lesson of the passage is a warning about –

Ⓐ   trying to be too powerful

Ⓑ   being too helpful

Ⓒ   playing mean tricks

Ⓓ   putting in too much effort

58   What is the main way the elephant and the whale are similar? What is the main way they are different? Write the **one** main similarly and the **one** main difference on the lines below.

Similarity: _____

_____

Difference: _____

_____

59   Why does the rabbit ask both the elephant and the whale to pull his cow out? Explain how this is a trick. Use **two** details from the passage in your answer.

_____

_____

_____

_____

_____

60   Describe the **two** ways the elephant and the whale try to punish the rabbit for tricking them.

1: _____

_____

2: _____

_____

Directions: This set has two passages in it. Read each passage and answer the questions that follow it. Then use both passages to answer the final question.

Introduction: Who has not heard of George Washington? It has been said of him that he was the "first in war, the first in peace, and first in the hearts of his countrymen." He was our most famous president. He has been called the Father of his Country. But George Washington's life almost took a different path.

Going to Sea

"I should like to be a sailor," said George Washington. "Then I could go to many strange lands and see many wonderful things. And, by and by, I might become the captain of a ship."

He was only fourteen years old. His older brothers were quite willing that he should go to sea. They said that a bright boy like George would not long be a common sailor. He would soon become a captain and then perhaps a great admiral.

And so the matter was at last settled. George's brothers knew the master of a trading ship who was getting ready to sail to England. He agreed to take the boy with him and teach him how to be a good sailor.

George's mother was very sad. His uncle had written her a letter saying:

"Do not let him go to sea. If he begins as a common sailor, he will never be anything else."

But George had made up his mind to go. He was headstrong and determined. He would not listen to anyone who tried to persuade him to stay at home. At last the day came for the ship to sail. It was waiting in the river. A boat was at the landing, ready to take him on board. The little chest that held his clothing had been carried down to the bank. George was in high glee at the thought of going.

"Goodbye, mother," he said.

He stood on the doorstep and looked back into the house. He saw the kind faces of those whom he loved. He began to feel very sad.

"Goodbye, my dear boy!"

George saw the tears in his mother's eyes. He saw them rolling down her cheeks. He knew that she did not wish him to go. He could not bear to see her grief.

He stood still for a moment, thinking. Then he turned quickly and said, "Mother, I have changed my mind. I will stay at home and do as you wish."

Then he called to his brother, who was waiting at the door, and said, "Samuel, run down to the shore and tell them not to put the chest in the boat. Send word to the captain not to wait for me, for I have changed my mind. I am not going to sea."

61   The main purpose of the introduction is to show that George Washington –

Ⓐ   is greatly respected

Ⓑ   is sometimes misunderstood

Ⓒ   was hardworking

Ⓓ   was brave and daring

62   Read this sentence from the passage.

They said that a bright boy like George would not long be a common sailor.

As it is used in the sentence, what does <u>bright</u> mean?

Ⓐ   clever

Ⓑ   shiny

Ⓒ   strong

Ⓓ   thoughtful

63   Read these sentences from the passage.

He was headstrong and determined. He would not listen to anyone who tried to persuade him to stay at home.

Which statement describes the relationship between the two sentences?

Ⓐ   The first sentence gives a fact and the second sentence gives an opinion.

Ⓑ   The first sentence states a problem and the second sentence describes a solution.

Ⓒ   The first sentence makes a claim and the second sentence gives a supporting detail.

Ⓓ   The first sentence describes a first event and the second sentence describes a second event.

64   Read this sentence from the passage.

George was in high glee at the thought of going.

What does the phrase "in high glee" mean?

Ⓐ   dressed well

Ⓑ   waiting in line

Ⓒ   sure of himself

Ⓓ   very happy

65   Why does George Washington decide not to go to sea?

Ⓐ   He feels sorry for his mother.

Ⓑ   He realizes that he can achieve more at home.

Ⓒ   He does not want to let his brothers down.

Ⓓ   He feels afraid of traveling far away.

66   How is the uncle's opinion on George Washington going to sea different from the brothers' opinion? Use **two** details from the passage in your answer.

_____

_____

_____

_____

_____

George Washington – The Father of the Nation

 George Washington was the first President of the United States of America. People often refer to him as the "Father of the Nation." He was a leader throughout his life. Washington only went to school until age 16. However, he realized how important learning was and so he read as many books as he could find. He also observed people he admired. In this way, he learned from others.

In 1775, Washington became Commander in Chief of the Continental Army. He did not get paid as a commander, but he felt it his duty to work for the country he believed in. He helped train more than 10,000 soldiers. As a commander, he greatly respected and cared for his soldiers. In 1776, he led the troops to cross the Delaware River. He took the city of Princeton. His troops fought until the end of the Revolutionary War in 1783.

His ability to make good decisions was another of his key skills. These decisions, his courage, and his strong belief in his troops helped him defeat the powerful British army. Finally, the British would no longer rule the colonies. The colonies could become an independent country.

In 1787, Washington went to the Constitutional Convention. He was elected President of the Convention. In an amazing show of support, all the other representatives voted for him. The convention was held in Philadelphia, Pennsylvania. This is when the United States Constitution was written. The Constitution talked about how the government would work and about independence for the colonies.

Then in 1789, voters chose the first president of the new country. They voted Washington as President of the United States. Washington realized that the way he acted as a president would be how other presidents after him would act. For this reason, he tried to always think what was best for the country. He also tried to be fair and honest in all his dealings. He won a second term in 1792.

During his presidency, the Bill of Rights was adopted. Many people think this is his greatest accomplishment. The Bill of Rights talks about freedoms for people. Some of these freedoms are freedom of religion and freedom of speech.

Washington turned down a third term for presidency. This decision made many people admire him even more. Washington thought that a third term would give him too much power. He left office in 1797 and moved to his Virginia plantation. He died there in 1799 at the age of 67.

67   How is the passage mainly organized?

    Ⓐ   A problem is described and then a solution is given.

    Ⓑ   Events are described in the order they occur.

    Ⓒ   Facts are given to support an argument.

    Ⓓ   A question is asked and then answered.

68   Which sentence from paragraph 4 best shows that George Washington was popular? Select the **one** best answer.

    ☐   *In 1787, Washington went to the Constitutional Convention.*

    ☐   *He was elected President of the Convention.*

    ☐   *In an amazing show of support, all the other representatives voted for him.*

    ☐   *The convention was held in Philadelphia, Pennsylvania.*

    ☐   *This is when the United States Constitution was written.*

    ☐   *The Constitution talked about how the government would work and about independence for the colonies.*

69   Which sentence best summarizes the main idea of paragraph 5?

    Ⓐ   Washington had nobody he could rely on.

    Ⓑ   Washington tried to set a good example.

    Ⓒ   Washington performed better than people expected.

    Ⓓ   Washington was proud of his successes.

70   According to the passage, what do many people think George Washington's greatest achievement was?

    Ⓐ   turning down a third presidency

    Ⓑ   having the Bill of Rights adopted

    Ⓒ   getting the Constitution written

    Ⓓ   defeating the British army

71   The first paragraph states that Washington learned from others. Describe **two** ways he learned from others.

    1: _____

    _____

    2: _____

    _____

Directions: Use both passages to answer the following question.

72   The introduction to the first passage states that George Washington's life "almost took a different path." How does the second passage show that this would have been a great shame? Use details from both passages to support your answer.

_____

_____

_____

_____

_____

_____

_____

_____

_____

_____

_____

_____

_____

_____

_____

_____

_____

End-of-Grade Reading

Practice Test 2

Session 1

Instructions

Read each passage and answer the questions that follow it.

For each multiple-choice question, fill in the circle for the correct answer. For other types of questions, follow the instructions given. Some of the questions require a written answer. Write your answer on the lines provided.

Everyday Life in Colonial Times

The Food in Olden Times

In old colonial times, our wheat bread was mostly unknown. Loaves were made of maize and rye, not unlike the brown bread of our time. Baked pumpkin with milk was a favorite dish. Bean porridge was always a common article of food, and in some parts of the country it is still popular. It was made by boiling beans with the liquor in which corned beef had been cooked. It was very convenient for wood-choppers in winter to carry a frozen piece of porridge in their pockets and thaw it out for dinner in the woods. The longer it was kept, the better it tasted. Hence the common rhyme, "Bean porridge hot, bean porridge cold; bean porridge in the pot; nine days old."

In well-to-do families, the cupboard or dresser shone with pewter plates, platters, and bowls. Square wooden plates were often used by average families. However, with some poorer families there was one common dish used. The whole family helped themselves from this one dish with their fingers.

Instead of forks, which were not known, they had thick and clumsy pewter spoons. These were easily broken, and they often had to be melted up and run over again into moulds. This was done by men who traveled from house to house for this purpose. In fact shoemakers, tailors, dressmakers, butchers, and other highly useful workers traveled about from one family to another in pursuit of work.

Schools in Olden Times

In most of the colonies, the settlers were hardly located in their new homes before they began to provide schools for their children. In 1635, the town of Boston "voted to entreat brother Philemon Pormont to become schoolmaster." Then in 1647, a law was passed which is still the foundation of the marvellous educational system of Massachusetts. This law stated that towns must create public schools to provide all children with a basic education.

Only six years after Boston was founded, the sum of two thousand dollars was set apart to found a new school at Cambridge. This school has now become Harvard University. For years afterwards, every family gave annually one peck of corn, or one shilling in money, to support the young college.

The schoolhouses were rough and crude. They usually had just one room. Within the room, the door and the big fireplace were on one side. Against the other three walls was a long, rough shelf, in front of which was a seat made of a split log with legs driven beneath. The pupils faced the wall with their backs to the teacher. In front was another lower bench filled by the younger pupils. The teacher sat near the middle of the room. The sessions were long and went for seven or eight hours a day. The boys had to furnish the firewood, and if any unlucky fellow failed to bring in his share, he had to sit in a cold corner for that day. When the fire was brisk, the scholars were almost roasted on one side and nearly frozen on the other.

The children each brought a few pennies a week for tuition. There were not many textbooks, and the supplies were very scanty. The students often learned to write on pieces of white bark.

Newspapers, Traveling, and the Night Watchman

 The first printing press was set up at Cambridge in 1639. It was used chiefly to print sermons and small pamphlets. The first newspaper published in America was the *Boston News-Letter* in 1704. It was a brown sheet hardly more than a foot square. It was put out weekly. News traveled slowly, for there was little communication between cities. Travelers were few, and transport was slow. In fact, a stage-coach that made forty miles a day between New York and Philadelphia was called, on account of its great speed, "the flying machine."

In the cities, news was announced in the daytime by the public crier. The public crier walked the streets ringing a large hand-bell. He paused at the corners, where he recited his message of a child lost, or a reward offered, or the happening of any important event. In the night the town watchman paced the streets with rattle and lantern. He would stop every person he met after nine o'clock to demand his or her name and business. He also called aloud the hours of the night in a sing-song tone: "Twelve o'clock and all's well."

Sometimes his night cry was intensely interesting. At Philadelphia in October, 1781, evening after evening everyone went to bed anxious about our army at Yorktown. People were hoping every hour to hear news of victory. One night the old watchman's cry was heard echoing along the lonely streets: "Two-o'clock and Cornwall's captured!" How the windows flew up! And how the hearty cheers burst along from house to house all through the city!

1   Why was bean porridge convenient for wood-choppers in winter?

    Ⓐ   It provided lots of energy.

    Ⓑ   There were lots of beans available.

    Ⓒ   It lasted a long time.

    Ⓓ   It was easy to make.

2   Complete the table below by describing the dinnerware most often used for each type of family.

Dinnerware Used by Colonial Families

Poor	Average	Wealthy

3   The passage describes how "shoemakers, tailors, dressmakers, butchers, and other workers" traveled to families seeking work. What do these workers have in common with the people who fixed pewter spoons?

    Ⓐ   They all provide a useful service.

    Ⓑ   They are all poorly paid.

    Ⓒ   They all help people make or eat food.

    Ⓓ   They are all highly experienced workers.

4 Which word in the first paragraph of the section titled "Schools in Olden Times" best shows that the author admires the school system of Massachusetts?

Ⓐ   *foundation*

Ⓑ   *marvelous*

Ⓒ   *provide*

Ⓓ   *basic*

5 According to the passage, how was Harvard University supported by all the people?

Ⓐ   Families paid for their children to attend classes.

Ⓑ   Families gave money or crops each year.

Ⓒ   Families decided what would be taught.

Ⓓ   Families provided textbooks and other materials.

6 Read this sentence from the passage.

The schoolhouses were rough and crude.

What does the word <u>crude</u> mean?

Ⓐ   basic

Ⓑ   cold

Ⓒ   loud

Ⓓ   small

7   Read these sentences from the passage.

> **There were not many textbooks, and the supplies were very scanty. The students often learned to write on pieces of white bark.**

Which term best describes the second sentence?

    Ⓐ   an opinion

    Ⓑ   a comparison

    Ⓒ   an example

    Ⓓ   a cause

8   According to the passage, when was the first newspaper published in America?

    Ⓐ   1639

    Ⓑ   1647

    Ⓒ   1704

    Ⓓ   1781

9   Complete the web below by listing **three** examples of common foods in colonial times.

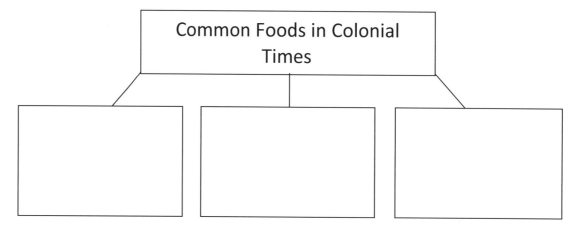

10   Based on the information in the section titled "The Food in Olden Times," list **two** problems with the pewter spoons used at the time.

1: _____

_____

2: _____

_____

11   Would learning at a schoolhouse in colonial times have been difficult? Use **two** details from the passage to support your answer.

_____

_____

_____

_____

_____

12   In the last paragraph, how does the author help the reader imagine the excitement of the people when learning that Cornwall had been captured? Use **two** details from the passage in your answer.

_____

_____

_____

_____

_____

Block City
by Robert Louis Stevenson

What are you able to build with your blocks?
Castles and palaces, temples and docks.
Rain may keep raining, and others go roam,
But I can be happy and building at home.

Let the sofa be mountains, the carpet be sea,
There I'll establish a city for me:
A kirk and a mill and a palace beside,
And a harbor as well where my vessels may ride.

Great is the palace with pillar and wall,
A sort of a tower on the top of it all,
And steps coming down in an orderly way
To where my toy vessels lie safe in the bay.

This one is sailing and that one is moored:
Hark to the song of the sailors on board!
And see on the steps of my palace, the kings
Coming and going with presents and things!

Now I have done with it, down let it go.
All in a moment the town is laid low,
Block upon block lying scattered and free,
What is there left of my town by the sea?

13 Which statement best describes how the poet starts the poem?

Ⓐ   by asking and answering a question

Ⓑ   by stating a problem and its solution

Ⓒ   by giving a fact and an opinion

Ⓓ   by making a statement and supporting it

14 Read these lines from the poem.

> **Rain may keep raining, and others go roam,**
> **But I can be happy and building at home.**

What do these lines suggest about the speaker?

Ⓐ   He prefers to play with blocks alone.

Ⓑ   He only plays with blocks when he has to.

Ⓒ   He wishes he could play with blocks more often.

Ⓓ   He is content to play with blocks.

15 What is the rhyme pattern of each stanza of the poem?

Ⓐ   There are two pairs of rhyming lines.

Ⓑ   The first and second lines rhyme.

Ⓒ   The first and last lines rhyme.

Ⓓ   None of the lines rhyme.

16 Read this line from the poem.

There I'll establish a city for me:

What does the word <u>establish</u> mean?

Ⓐ   build

Ⓑ   destroy

Ⓒ   discover

Ⓓ   name

17 In the fourth stanza, the poet refers to "toy vessels." What are the toy vessels?

Ⓐ   boats

Ⓑ   cars

Ⓒ   planes

Ⓓ   trains

18 Based on your answer to Question 17, circle **three** words from the fifth stanza that show what the toy vessels are. Circle the **three** words below.

This one is sailing and that one is moored:

Hark to the song of the sailors on board!

And see on the steps of my palace, the kings

Coming and going with presents and things!

19   Which line from the fourth stanza helps readers imagine the sound of the city?

Ⓐ   *This one is sailing and that one is moored:*

Ⓑ   *Hark to the song of the sailors on board!*

Ⓒ   *And see on the steps of my palace, the kings*

Ⓓ   *Coming and going with presents and things!*

20   The last stanza of the poem describes the town as "laid low." What is the phrase "laid low" an example of?

Ⓐ   personification, describing objects as if they have human qualities

Ⓑ   symbolism, using an object to stand for something else

Ⓒ   hyperbole, overstating the qualities of something to make a point

Ⓓ   alliteration, repeating consonant sounds in neighboring words

21   Which object mentioned in the poem does the photograph mainly represent?

Ⓐ   dock

Ⓑ   mill

Ⓒ   mountains

Ⓓ   palace

22   Based on the poem, how would the author of the poem be most likely to describe building with blocks?

    Ⓐ   as a creative activity

    Ⓑ   as a challenging activity

    Ⓒ   as a physical activity

    Ⓓ   as an educational activity

23   List **two** details from the second stanza that show that the speaker is using his imagination when playing with the blocks.

1: _____

_____

2: _____

_____

24   How do you think the speaker feels about the town being knocked down in the last stanza? Use **two** details from the poem to support your answer.

_____

_____

_____

_____

Please Leave the Library Alone

Thomas Smith was a twelve-year-old that grew up in the small town of Gosling. He heard that the mayor wanted to knock down the local library and put up a theater instead. Thomas had a lot of memories at the library and did not want it to be knocked down. He was determined to do something about it. His mother told him that he should write a letter to Mayor Bixby to let him know how he feels.

Here is that letter:

Dear Mayor Bixby,

I know you plan to knock down the Goldstein Library this winter. I know you want more people to visit this part of town and you think a theater will do the trick. I think you are right, but, I do not think you should tear down the library. I am asking you, please leave the library alone.

The library was very important to me as I was growing up. The library is where I spent many summers playing with other kids. I learned how to read at the library and I wrote my first short story. I met my best friend, Stephanie, there. Most importantly, I check out books there to learn about more things.

Also, many kids I go to school with also love the Goldstein Library. They all have memories there like I do. Many adults I have talked to also love the Goldstein Library and would be sad to see it go. So, please, leave the library alone.

If you have ever been to the library, you would know they have more than just books. They have a book on display that was checked out by Katy Perry before she was a famous singer! They also have a lamp that was donated by Taylor Swift and a table that was once Frank Sinatra's. What I am trying to say is, that there is a lot of history in the Goldstein Library.

The Goldstein Library has also been a home for some people, like me! When I was seven, there was a bad storm that did a lot of damage to my home. We had nowhere to stay, just like many other people we knew. The owners of the Goldstein Library were glad to take us in while the repairs were being done. I cannot imagine walking past a movie theater and thinking "I lived here once."

I guess I do not understand why you are not putting the theater up on the corner that is only two blocks away from the library. You do not need to knock anything down to build there and you could see the theater lights from miles away. It could be amazing!

I think you should take time and think about your plan. It is okay if you decide that the library is not the best place for a movie theater. Yes, it is a big space. Yes, a lot of people walk past it every day. Yes, not many people use libraries now. That does not mean there are not better choices.

I am sure that the owners of the Goldstein Library would be happy to turn the library into a museum. I only ask that we can still check out books. Please, Mayor Bixby, leave the library alone!

From,

Thomas Smith

Thomas sent his letter to the mayor. A few days later, the mayor visited his school and asked to speak with the class. When the mayor asked if anyone had a story they would like to share about the library, nearly everyone put up their hand. Every kid in the class had a story to tell about a memory they had at the Goldstein Library. The mayor listened carefully to every story he was told.

A few kids even met their favorite celebrity there. Some famous people would sign books and posters at the Goldstein Library. Thomas got to meet his favorite wrestler there.

When the Mayor heard that everyone loved the library, he did not build a theater there. But, he did not leave it alone. He made it a historical landmark so that it could stay forever. The mayor wanted his children and grandchildren to make memories at the Goldstein Library for years to come.

After the library was changed to a museum, Thomas and his friends went there on a field trip. They checked out books. They had lunch at the Frank Sinatra table. There was a ceremony that was a surprise.

The owners of the library set up a stage. They asked Thomas to come up. They held a giant red ribbon in front of Thomas. They gave him giant scissors for him to cut the ribbon. He cut the ribbon and everyone cheered.

They also put in a bench with a sign over it. The sign read "Thanks to Thomas Smith, the Mayor left the library alone." Thomas visits the library every Saturday. He sits on his bench and reads his favorite books to younger kids. He makes new memories every weekend, and he never worries about the future of the library.

25   According to the passage, what did the mayor want to put up in place of the library?

Ⓐ   mall

Ⓑ   park

Ⓒ   school

Ⓓ   theater

26   The photograph at the beginning of the passage mainly makes Thomas look –

Ⓐ   brave

Ⓑ   cranky

Ⓒ   determined

Ⓓ   nervous

27   Which detail best explains why Thomas did not want the library knocked down?

Ⓐ   He is twelve years old.

Ⓑ   He grew up in Gosling.

Ⓒ   He has a lot of memories of the library.

Ⓓ   He loves reading and cannot afford many books.

28   Read this sentence from the passage.

> *I know you want more people to visit this part of town and you think a theater will do the trick.*

What does the phrase "do the trick" mean?

Ⓐ   achieve the result

Ⓑ   change everything

Ⓒ   make people laugh

Ⓓ   earn more money

29   Which sentence would be the best caption for the photograph of the students?

Ⓐ   *A few days later, the mayor visited his school and asked to speak with the class.*

Ⓑ   *When the mayor asked if anyone had a story they would like to share about the library, nearly everyone put up their hand.*

Ⓒ   *Every kid in the class had a story to tell about a memory they had at the Goldstein Library.*

Ⓓ   *The mayor listened carefully to every story he was told.*

30   The passage describes how a ceremony was held for Thomas. How would he most likely feel during the ceremony?

Ⓐ   annoyed

Ⓑ   curious

Ⓒ   embarrassed

Ⓓ   proud

31   Which of these would be the best title for the passage?

    Ⓐ   Books for Everyone

    Ⓑ   Why Libraries Matter

    Ⓒ   Growing up in Gosling

    Ⓓ   Thomas Saves the Library

32   The main lesson that readers can learn from the actions of Thomas is about –

    Ⓐ   making a difference

    Ⓑ   valuing the little things

    Ⓒ   showing kindness to others

    Ⓓ   being willing to try new things

33   Complete the web with **two** more examples of reasons the library was important to Thomas as he was growing up.

He spent summers playing there.		
	Why the Library is Important to Thomas	
He met his best friend there.		

34   Complete the table by writing the item related to each famous person.

Special Items in the Goldstein Library

Person	Item
Katy Perry	
Taylor Swift	
Frank Sinatra	

35   According to the passage, how was the library a home once? Use **two** details from the passage in your answer.

_____

_____

_____

_____

_____

36 How is the outcome of Thomas's letter even better than he expected? Use at least **two** details from the passage to support your answer.

_____

_____

_____

_____

_____

_____

_____

_____

_____

_____

_____

_____

_____

_____

_____

_____

_____

_____

End-of-Grade Reading

Practice Test 2

Session 2

Instructions

Read each passage and answer the questions that follow it.

For each multiple-choice question, fill in the circle for the correct answer. For other types of questions, follow the instructions given. Some of the questions require a written answer. Write your answer on the lines provided.

Barry's Favorite Dinner

Barry was getting ready for school when he told his mom that he wanted to have a few friends over for dinner. She agreed and asked what he wanted to have for dinner. He told her that he wanted to have his favorite.

On the bus ride to school, Barry asked his friends Tucker, Damon, and Joseph to come over for dinner. They all said yes right away. Then, they asked what was for dinner. He told them his mom was making his favorite. They asked what his favorite meal was, and he smiled and said it was a surprise.

Tucker, Damon, and Joseph started to worry. They each had a food that they hated. Tucker hated spaghetti, Damon hated hamburgers, and Joseph hated salad. All day, each friend tried to figure out what was going to be for dinner.

Tucker's Investigation

Tucker sat down next to Barry at lunch. Tucker had chocolate pudding cup, something he knew Barry liked.

"Barry," Tucker said. "What will it take for you to tell me what's for dinner?"

"I think you know what we are having for dinner, Tucker," Barry replied.

"Well, I am sure you have told me what your favorite is, but I can't remember. You can tell me, I swear I won't tell Damon and Joseph," Tucker said.

"You really don't remember?"

"I will give you this pudding cup if you tell me," Tucker offered.

"You have yourself a deal," Barry replied, taking the pudding cup. "Well, you remember when you came over for dinner right before Christmas?" he asked.

"Yes…" Tucker said slowly.

"Do you remember what we had for dinner?" Barry asked.

"Liver and onions?" Tucker said with a frown.

Barry hid his grin and stopped himself laughing by taking a bite of his sandwich.

Damon's Demands

Damon saw Barry sitting by himself at recess. Damon had a special bookmark he knew Barry liked.

"Barry," Damon said. "I really want to know what we are having for dinner."

"I think you know what we are having for dinner, Damon," Barry replied.

"I am pretty sure we had your favorite at my house, but we have had a lot of dinners at my house. I can't remember which one," Damon said.

"You really don't remember?" Barry asked.

"I do not," Damon said. "But, I will give you that bookmark you like if you tell me! I swear I won't tell Joseph or Tucker."

"Fine," Barry replied. "We are having sushi."

"Raw fish?" Damon asked.

"Yep!" Barry replied. Sushi was way worse than hamburgers.

Joseph's Interview

Joseph saw Barry sitting alone on the bus in the back. Joseph needed to find out what Barry was serving for dinner. He had a cool gel pen that wrote in black glitter that Barry often asked to borrow.

"Hey buddy," Joseph said as he sat next to Barry.

"Hi," Barry replied.

"So, listen, I really want to know what we are having for dinner tonight."

"You, too?" Barry asked.

"Did you tell Damon and Tucker?" Joseph asked.

"Well, sort of," Barry replied.

"What do you mean by that?" Joseph asked.

"I told them something," Barry replied. "But, I might have not told them the whole truth."

"What did you tell them?" Joseph asked.

"Well, I told Tucker we are having liver and onions. Then, I told Damon that we were having sushi."

"Well, which is the truth?" Joseph asked. "I will give you this cool gel pen if you tell me the truth."

"Okay, I'll tell you the truth," Barry replied. "We are having roasted duck and mashed pumpkin."

"Really?" Joseph asked.

"Yep!" Barry replied. Roasted duck with mashed pumpkin was way worse than salad.

The Dinner

Tucker, Damon, and Joseph were not looking forward to the terrible dinners that Barry had described. However, they got to Barry's house on time, since they had agreed to come to dinner. They each took a seat at the table. Each of Barry's friends looked nervous.

"Okay, everyone!" Barry announced. "I know you are expecting liver and onions, sushi, and roasted duck with mashed pumpkin." At this, each friend looked confused. "We are actually having *all three!*"

The boys looked nervously at each other. Barry continued, "I'm just kidding guys! We are having hamburger spaghetti with a house salad!" The boys still looked nervous. "Get your plates, let's go to the kitchen!"

Each boy picked up their plate and headed to the kitchen. As they went through the door, a fantastic and familiar smell filled their nostrils. *Pizza*. A smile spread across each boy's face.

"I can't believe you guys forgot that pizza was my favorite!" Barry exclaimed. "I only talk about it *every* time they are serving anything other than pizza for lunch!" The boys laughed and filled their plates with cheesy pizza.

37   Who is most likely represented in the first photograph in the passage?

    Ⓐ   Barry

    Ⓑ   Damon

    Ⓒ   Joseph

    Ⓓ   Tucker

38   The second paragraph states that "Tucker, Damon, and Joseph started to worry." What are Tucker, Damon, and Joseph worried about?

    Ⓐ   whether there will be enough food for everyone

    Ⓑ   whether they will like the food

    Ⓒ   whether they all should go to Barry's house

    Ⓓ   whether Barry is going to cook the food

39   In the section titled "Damon's Demands," how does Damon feel when Barry says they are having sushi?

    Ⓐ   confused

    Ⓑ   disappointed

    Ⓒ   excited

    Ⓓ   frightened

40   Which sentence from the first paragraph of the section titled "The Dinner" best supports the idea that Barry's friends are polite?

    Ⓐ   *Tucker, Damon, and Joseph were not looking forward to the terrible dinners that Barry had described.*

    Ⓑ   *However, they got to Barry's house on time, since they had agreed to come to dinner.*

    Ⓒ   *They each took a seat at the table.*

    Ⓓ   *Each of Barry's friends looked nervous.*

41   Read this sentence from the passage.

As they went through the door, a fantastic and familiar smell filled their nostrils.

What does the word <u>familiar</u> show about the smell?

    Ⓐ   They knew it well.

    Ⓑ   They liked it a lot.

    Ⓒ   It was strong.

    Ⓓ   It made them feel hungry.

42   When does the turning point of the passage occur?

    Ⓐ   when Barry invites his friends for dinner

    Ⓑ   when Barry tells Tucker what is for dinner

    Ⓒ   when Barry's friends arrive at his house

    Ⓓ   when Barry's friends smell the pizza

43   Which word best describes the passage overall?

  Ⓐ   lighthearted

  Ⓑ   meaningful

  Ⓒ   scary

  Ⓓ   serious

44   At the end of the section titled "Tucker's Investigation," the author describes how Barry hid his grin and tried not to laugh. Explain what Barry finds funny. Use **two** details from the passage to support your answer.

_____

_____

_____

_____

45 Near the end of the passage, Barry tells his friends they are having "hamburger spaghetti with a house salad." Why does Barry say they are having those three foods? Explain your answer.

_____

_____

_____

_____

_____

46 Complete the web below by listing the **three** items that Barry gets from his friends for giving them information.

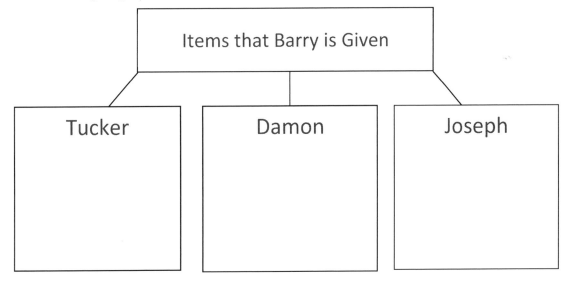

47   Complete the table below by listing what Barry tells each friend they are having for dinner.

Friend	What Barry Says is for Dinner
Tucker	
Damon	
Joseph	

48   How do you think Barry's friends feel when they see they are having pizza for dinner? Use **two** details from the passage to support your answer.

_____

_____

_____

_____

_____

Forests of the World

Forests are beautiful, peaceful, and mysterious. They provide us with fresh cool air and clean water. Millions of plants and animals live in the forest. Without forests our world would not survive.

Clean Air

Forests are like big air conditioners. The plants in forests take in carbon dioxide. They then make oxygen and release it into the air. Forests trap all the ash, dust, pollen, and smoke in the air. The large trees also absorb water through their roots. Then they release the water into the air through their leaves. That's why the air in forests always feels nice and cool.

Clean Water

Forests catch rain on the forest floor and on the canopy. The canopy is the very tops of the trees. The trees filter and clean the water and the tree roots help remove the dirt and smoke too. More than half the drinking water in the United States is from forests.

Wonderful Wildlife

An amazing variety of animals can be found in forests. Millions of species need forests to survive. In the United States, more than 550 species of aquatic life depend on the rivers that run through forests. Some very special animals live on land in American forests too. Black bears, hundreds of different types of butterflies, and woodpeckers are some of them. There are around 70 species of birds that live in American pine forests.

In the United States, there are 155 national forests in 42 states. But not all forests are the same. There are three main types of forest in the world. These are tropical, temperate, and boreal.

Temperate Forests

Temperate forests mainly have deciduous trees. Deciduous trees are ones that lose their leaves in fall. They are usually tall with broad leaves. Oak, beech, and walnut trees are some of the trees in these forests. Lots of small mammals and birds live here too. Squirrels, raccoons, deer, and even black bears can live in this type of forest. Temperate forests have cold winters and hot summers. As well as being in the United States, temperate forests are found in Europe, New Zealand, Australia, and Asia.

Boreal Forests

Boreal forests are the biggest type of forest. They have long cold winters and receive little rain. They have trees with needle-shaped leaves. Pine, fir, and hemlock trees are some of them. These are called coniferous trees because they have cones. Large animals like moose, wolves, caribou, and bears live here. There are also small animals like mice, rabbits, lynxes, and minks. Boreal forests are found in North America, Europe, and Asia.

Tropical Forests

The smallest type of forest is tropical. Tropical forests are mainly around the equator. The equator is around the middle of the earth. Places on the equator are usually hotter. Tropical forests are warm throughout the year and get a lot of rain. It rains most of the year in some tropical forests. Even when it is not raining there is often a fog keeping the plants damp. Tropical forests have over half of the world's plant and insect species living in them. And there may still be millions of species that haven't been discovered yet. The trees that grow here don't lose their leaves. They are evergreen. The forests are thick with big and small plants.

One special type of forest is called a rainforest. Most rainforests are tropical forests, but some are temperate. One temperate rainforest is the Coast Redwood Forest in Redwood National Park, California. Another one is the Westland Temperate Rainforest in New Zealand.

The Coast Redwood Forest, California

The largest trees on earth grow in this forest. Coast redwoods can grow 330 feet tall and can be thousands of years old. This forest is also part of the largest temperate rainforest on earth. It is so large because it is made up of smaller forests stretching from Alaska to California. The Coast Redwood Forest is right along the coast looking out to sea. Because it is next to coastal mountains it rains a lot. Most of the year fog keeps the forest cool and wet too. Lots of small mammals and birds live here.

The Westland Temperate Rainforest

Across the other side of the world on the west coast of New Zealand is another temperate rainforest. The Westland Temperate Rainforest also runs along the coast, next to mountains. It has a huge amount of rain and 57 glaciers. A glacier is huge area of ice and snow that stays for hundreds of years. The trees in this forest are not as tall as the redwoods in California, but they are still ancient giants. Totara trees grow to 98 feet and have huge trunks. They can be hundreds of years old.

The forest is also filled with rare ferns and plants. The Westland Temperate Rainforest has very different birds to the Californian forest. Some of them are only found in New Zealand, like the kiwi, pukeko, fantail, and kea. There are giant snails and rare beetles. There are spiders that hide in holes on the ground instead of making webs.

Kiwis are flightless birds found in New Zealand.

The Westland Rainforest does have a few small mammals like rats, cats, possums, and stoats which are not native to New Zealand. They are pests and kill native birds. They also damage the trees and plants.

For a healthy planet, we need our forests. They might be dense and lush tropical forests. Or boreal woodlands filled with animals. They might be temperate rainforests next to the sea. Whatever type they are, forests are amazing places that we need to protect.

49   What does the first paragraph summarize?

Ⓐ   how beautiful forests are

Ⓑ   why forests are important

Ⓒ   how many types of forests there are

Ⓓ   why forests are in danger

50   Complete the diagram to summarize the information in the section titled "Clean Air."

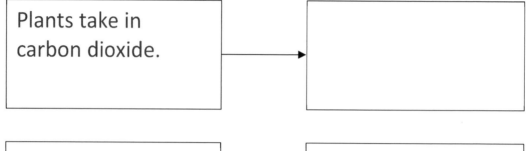

Plants take in carbon dioxide.	→	

Trees absorb water through their roots.	→	

51   Read this sentence from the passage.

The canopy is the very tops of the trees.

Which term best describes this sentence?

Ⓐ   a definition

Ⓑ   an example

Ⓒ   an instruction

Ⓓ   an opinion

52   Read this sentence from the passage.

> **In the United States, more than 550 species of aquatic life depend on the rivers that run through forests.**

What does the word <u>aquatic</u> mean?

Ⓐ   breathes in air

Ⓑ   seen mostly at night

Ⓒ   lives in water

Ⓓ   eats only plants

53   How are the sections titled "Clean Air," "Clean Water," and "Wonderful Wildlife" similar?

Ⓐ   They explain why animals need forests.

Ⓑ   They compare different types of forests.

Ⓒ   They describe the benefits of forests.

Ⓓ   They encourage people to visit forests.

54   Which sentence best supports the idea that tropical forests are important for wildlife?

Ⓐ   *The smallest type of forest is tropical.*

Ⓑ   *Tropical forests are mainly around the equator.*

Ⓒ   *It rains most of the year in some tropical forests.*

Ⓓ   *Tropical forests have over half of the world's plant and insect species living in them.*

55 Which sentence about the Coast Redwood Forest could best be supported by including a map?

Ⓐ   *The largest trees on earth grow in this forest.*

Ⓑ   *Coast redwoods can grow 330 feet tall and can be thousands of years old.*

Ⓒ   *It is so large because it is made up of smaller forests stretching from Alaska to California.*

Ⓓ   *Most of the year fog keeps the forest cool and wet too.*

56 What does the photograph of the coast redwood trees emphasize about them?

Ⓐ   their age

Ⓑ   their height

Ⓒ   their beauty

Ⓓ   their importance

57 Select the correct box to show which type of forest the trees listed are found in.

Trees Common to Temperate and Boreal Forests

Tree	Temperate Forests	Boreal Forests
Beech	☐	☐
Fir	☐	☐
Hemlock	☐	☐
Oak	☐	☐
Pine	☐	☐
Walnut	☐	☐

58   Write a brief definition of each term used in the passage.

Coniferous: _____

Deciduous: _____

Evergreen: _____

59   How is the weather of a tropical forest different from the weather of a boreal forest? Use **two** details from the passage in your answer.

_____

_____

_____

_____

_____

60   List **two** ways the Coast Redwood Forest and the Westland Temperate Rainforest are similar.

1: _____

_____

2: _____

_____

Directions: This set has two passages in it. Read each passage and answer the questions that follow it. Then use both passages to answer the final question.

The Snowdrop
by Hans Christian Andersen

The snow lay deep, for it was wintertime. The winter winds blew cold, but there was one house where all was snug and warm. And in the house lay a little flower. In its bulb it lay, under the earth and the snow.

One day the rain fell and it trickled through the ice and snow down into the ground. And presently a sunbeam, pointed and slender, pierced down through the earth, and tapped on the bulb.

"Come in," said the flower.

"I can't do that," said the sunbeam. "I'm not strong enough to lift the latch. I shall be stronger when springtime comes."

"When will it be spring?" asked the flower of every little sunbeam that rapped on its door.

But for a long time it was winter. The ground was still covered with snow, and every night there was ice in the water. The flower grew quite tired of waiting.

"How long it is!" it said. "I feel quite cramped. I must stretch myself and rise up a little. I must lift the latch, and look out, and say 'good-morning' to the spring."

So the flower pushed and pushed. The walls were softened by the rain and warmed by the little sunbeams, so the flower shot up from under the snow, with a pale green bud on its stalk and some long narrow leaves on either side. It was biting cold.

"You are a little too early," said the wind and the weather, but every sunbeam sang. "Welcome," sang the sunbeam, and the flower raised its head from the snow and unfolded itself – pure and white, and decked with green stripes.

It was weather to freeze it to pieces, for it was such a delicate little flower, but it was stronger than anyone knew. It stood in its white dress in the white snow, bowing its head when the snowflakes fell, and raising it again to smile at the sunbeams, and every day it grew sweeter.

"Oh!" shouted the children, as they ran into the garden. "See the snowdrop! There it stands so pretty, so beautiful. It is the first, the only one!"

61   Read this sentence from the passage.

> **The winter winds blew cold, but there was one house where all was snug and warm.**

The use of the word <u>snug</u> mainly makes the house seem –

Ⓐ   cozy

Ⓑ   cramped

Ⓒ   lively

Ⓓ   quiet

62   Why does the flower decide to shoot up from under the snow?

Ⓐ   It is curious about what winter looks like.

Ⓑ   It is tired of waiting for it to get warmer.

Ⓒ   It is feeling afraid of being stuck underground.

Ⓓ   It is lonely and wants to be with the sun, wind, and rain.

63   What is the main problem the flower has to overcome in the passage?

Ⓐ   hard ground

Ⓑ   cold weather

Ⓒ   mean wind

Ⓓ   rough children

64   What quality makes the snowdrop in the passage special?

Ⓐ   curiosity

Ⓑ   determination

Ⓒ   kindness

Ⓓ   patience

65   In the last paragraph, how do the children feel about seeing the snowdrop?

Ⓐ   concerned

Ⓑ   excited

Ⓒ   puzzled

Ⓓ   shocked

66   The last paragraph describes how the snowdrop is "the only one." Why do you think the snowdrop is the only one? Use details from the passage to support your answer.

_____

_____

_____

_____

_____

The Three Little Butterfly Brothers
by Hans Christian Andersen

There were once three little butterfly brothers, one pink, one red, and one yellow. They played in the sunshine, and danced among the flowers in the garden, and they never grew tired because they were so happy.

One day there came a heavy rain, and it wet their wings. They flew away home, but when they got there they found the door locked and the key gone. So they had to stay out of doors in the rain, and they grew wetter and wetter.

They flew to the red and yellow tulips, and said: "Friend Tulips, will you open your flower cup and let us in till the storm is over?"

The tulips answered: "The red and yellow butterflies may enter, because they are like us, but the pink one may not come in."

But the red and yellow butterflies said: "If our white brother may not find shelter in your flower cup, why, then, we'll stay outside in the rain with him."

It rained harder and harder, and the poor little butterflies grew wetter and wetter, so they flew to the pink lily and said: "Good Lily, will you open your bud so we may creep in out of the rain?"

The lily answered: "The pink butterfly may come in, because he is like me, but the red and yellow ones must stay outside in the storm."

Then the little pink butterfly said: "If you won't receive my red and yellow brothers, why, then, I'll stay out in the rain with them. We would rather be wet than be parted."

So the three little butterflies flew away.

But the sun, who was behind a cloud, heard it all, and he knew what good little brothers the butterflies were, and how they had held together in spite of the wet. So he pushed his face through the clouds, and chased away the rain, and shone brightly on the garden.

He dried the wings of the three little butterflies, and warmed their bodies. They ceased to sorrow, and danced among the flowers till evening, then they flew away home, and found the door wide open.

67   Why is the rain important to the plot of the passage?

     (A)   It tells why the butterflies are happy.

     (B)   It explains why the butterflies need shelter.

     (C)   It shows how the butterflies enjoy nature.

     (D)   It explains why the butterflies are far from home.

68   Which word best describes how the butterflies act toward each other?

     (A)   greedy

     (B)   honest

     (C)   jealous

     (D)   loyal

69   What does the photograph near the start of the passage help readers understand?

     (A)   why the tulips turned the butterflies away

     (B)   how the butterflies felt about the tulips

     (C)   how the butterflies hoped to shelter inside the tulip's flower

     (D)   why the butterflies needed help from the tulips

70   Complete the table below by listing which butterflies the tulips and the lily will not help and why.

	Which Butterflies are not Helped	Why the Butterflies are not Helped
tulips		
lily		

71   How does the sun reward the butterflies for sticking together? Use **two** details from the passage in your answer.

_____

_____

_____

_____

_____

Directions: Use both passages to answer the following question.

72   How is the role of the sun similar in the two passages? Use details from both passages to support your answer.

_____

_____

_____

_____

_____

_____

_____

_____

_____

_____

_____

_____

_____

_____

_____

_____

End-of-Grade Reading

Practice Test 3

Session 1

Instructions

Read each passage and answer the questions that follow it.

For each multiple-choice question, fill in the circle for the correct answer. For other types of questions, follow the instructions given. Some of the questions require a written answer. Write your answer on the lines provided.

Harold and Arthur

Ever since Harold was a little boy, around three or four, he would reach for every crayon or paintbrush he saw. When most kids wanted cars or dolls, Harold wanted drawing paper and oil pastels.

For his eleventh birthday, Harold got a set of nice paint brushes and new watercolors. Since his birthday, he had painted oranges, apple trees, and even his house. His mom's birthday was coming up, so, he wanted to paint her something special.

After a lot of thinking, he decided he was going to paint her a picture of her favorite bird. He drew a cardinal flying through the air. Below it, he drew a field of her favorite flowers, yellow tulips. The sky had fluffy white clouds and in the distance Harold drew a farmhouse. Around the house he drew a long, white fence.

Harold erased the lines so that he could barely see them. First, Harold worked on the field of tulips. He spent many hours getting the colors just right. He had to be very careful to not let the colors bleed together since the grass was green and the tulips were yellow.

Once the bottom half of the painting was almost dry, Harold wanted to show it to his little brother, Arthur. Arthur was six and loved to play sports. Sometimes he feels left out because Harold never wanted to play sports, but only wanted to color.

Harold told Arthur that the painting was for their mother. Harold put the painting on his painting desk to dry completely. Arthur liked the painting that Harold was giving their mom for her birthday. Arthur did not have anything he could make, so he decided he wanted to add to Harold's painting.

Arthur got a black marker out of Harold's desk. He knew their mom liked airplane rides, so he tried to draw an airplane in the sky. The wing looked crooked so he did not draw the rest.

Arthur also knew that his mother liked going to the beach when it was sunny, so he started to draw a circle in the sky. He drew half of it and realized it was crooked. Arthur did not draw the rest of the sun.

Arthur felt like he had ruined Harold's painting, so he hid the black marker under his pillow and went to the kitchen for a snack. He chose peanut butter crackers and a glass of milk.

Arthur was watching cartoons on TV when he heard Harold cry out. Arthur knew he must have seen his ruined painting. He decided to stay in the living room and pretend he was asleep.

A few minutes later, Harold came into the living room and woke up Arthur. Arthur yawned and stretched, as if he had been asleep.

"Arthur, do you know what happened to my painting?" Harold asked.

"Is it missing?" Arthur asked.

"No, someone drew on it with black marker," Harold said.

"Oh, I did not know that," Arthur lied.

"I think you are lying," Harold said. Arthur acted shocked.

"What? Why?" Arthur asked.

"Because I found the black marker under your pillow," Harold said, holding the marker in the air. Arthur sat across from his brother silently. "Why did you do it?"

"I just wanted to help," Arthur said.

"You could have told me, Arthur. I would have let you help," Harold said.

"Sorry," Arthur said sadly.

"It's okay," Harold said. "I might be able to fix it."

Harold went back to his painting desk and looked at the squiggles of black marker. He noticed the line that Arthur drew trying to make a sun almost followed his line for a cloud. He used the black marker to complete the outline of that cloud. For balance, he outlined one of the clouds on the right.

Then he noticed that the line in the middle that should have been a plane wing almost matched the shape of the bird wing. Harold would just need to redraw the bird in a different position. He outlined the entire bird in black marker for contrast and balance.

Harold spent the next few hours painting the rest of his and Arthur's painting. It was different than every other painting he had done. He had never done black marker outlines before filling them with watercolor. He was not sure how he felt about how it looked.

The next day, it was their mother's birthday. They brought her breakfast in bed with a yellow tulip in a tall, skinny vase. Their father gave her a pretty gold necklace that she loved. Next, Harold gave her the painting from him and Arthur.

Harold told his mother what Arthur had added to the painting. Arthur told her that he tried to draw a plane and sun but did not know how. Harold also told his mother that he did not know how he felt about how it looked.

Their mother hugged her boys tightly and thanked them for the lovely picture with all her favorite things. She told Arthur it was very thoughtful of him to think of her. She told Harold that she loved the look of the black marker outlines and that this was her favorite painting ever because it was created by her two favorite people.

1   What is the main purpose of the first paragraph?

 Ⓐ to tell readers the main problem

 Ⓑ to explain why the events take place

 Ⓒ to introduce the main character

 Ⓓ to show the setting of the events

2   What does the photograph at the start of the passage suggest about Harold?

 Ⓐ He takes painting seriously.

 Ⓑ He has been painting for a long time.

 Ⓒ He often paints gifts for people.

 Ⓓ He enjoys different types of painting.

3   Read these sentences from the passage.

> **First, Harold worked on the field of tulips. He spent many hours getting the colors just right.**

What do these sentences suggest?

 Ⓐ Harold is learning a new skill.

 Ⓑ Harold wants the painting to be perfect.

 Ⓒ Harold wants Arthur to help him.

 Ⓓ Harold has never painted tulips before.

4   Circle the **two** items that Arthur tries to add to Harold's painting.

airplane   clouds   sun

farmhouse   fence   flowers

5   According to the passage, why doesn't Arthur finish what he starts to draw on the painting?

Ⓐ   He falls asleep while he is drawing.

Ⓑ   He wants to let Harold finish it.

Ⓒ   He loses his black marker.

Ⓓ   He doesn't draw each item well.

6   Select the **two** sentences that best support your answer to Question 5.

☐   *Arthur got a black marker out of Harold's desk.*

☐   *He knew their mom liked airplane rides, so he tried to draw an airplane in the sky.*

☐   *The wing looked crooked so he did not draw the rest.*

☐   *Arthur also knew that his mother liked going to the beach when it was sunny, so he started to draw a circle in the sky.*

☐   *He drew half of it and realized it was crooked.*

☐   *Arthur did not draw the rest of the sun.*

7   Read these sentences from the passage.

"It's okay," Harold said. "I might be able to fix it."

Which word means about the same as <u>fix</u>?

Ⓐ   change

Ⓑ   explain

Ⓒ   hide

Ⓓ   repair

8   The photograph of Arthur on the second page mainly suggests that he feels –

Ⓐ   amused

Ⓑ   embarrassed

Ⓒ   guilty

Ⓓ   proud

9   Which of these would be the best title for the passage?

Ⓐ   The Perfect Painting

Ⓑ   How to Paint a Picture

Ⓒ   Why I Love to Paint

Ⓓ   The Case of the Missing Painting

10   Read these sentences from the passage.

> **It was different than every other painting he had done. He had never done black marker outlines before filling them with watercolor.**

Why does Harold do black marker outlines in this painting? Use **two** details from the passage in your answer.

_____

_____

_____

_____

_____

11   Describe **two** details that show that Harold is understanding when he learns that Arthur has drawn on his painting.

1: _____

_____

2: _____

_____

12 Why do you think the mother likes the painting so much? Use **two** details from the passage to support your answer.

_____

_____

_____

_____

_____

_____

Snowkiting

The fresh icy wind blows down from the mountain. Clean white snow stretches out in every direction. Flying through the air, a kite skier flips and twists. It's like there is no gravity. Finally they land with a soft bump and zoom down the hill.

Snowkiting (or kite skiing) is becoming more popular in the United States. In winter, most ski fields and frozen lakes will have some colorful kites flying above them. Snowkite competitions have begun all around the world to find the fastest and the best. Freestyle snowkiters flip and twist. Long distance snowkiters race over the snow-covered hills.

Early Snowkiting

Snowkiting began in the United States when some skiers started experimenting with parachutes. Normally skiers need a snowy slope up in the mountains because they can only travel downhill. The skiers experimenting with kites found they could be pulled along by the wind. It even worked on flat ground. They tried skiing across frozen lakes and over small hills.

Then people in Europe started snowkiting. A lot of water kiteboarders thought it looked fun. (Kiteboarders are like surfers with kites.) In the summer they could kiteboard and in winter they could snowkite. People loved it! It became a proper sport in Europe. People started to run competitions. Now there are worldwide snowkiting competitions.

What is Snowkiting?

Snowkiting is a bit like sailing. It's also a bit like skiing. And it's a bit like flying a kite. When people snowkite, they stand on skis or on a snowboard. They hold onto the kite. The kite catches the wind and pulls them along. Snowkiting is exciting and pretty easy to learn. Most people learn how to snowkite in just a day. Kiteboarding on the water is much harder to learn. On the water, you sink. It's hard to get up and stay up on the board. On the snow or ice, you start standing up. All you need to do is hold on to the kite!

Snowkiting can be done on any snowy surface or frozen lake. There is no need to travel to a snowfield in the mountains or pay for access to special snowfields. There is no need to pay for ski lifts to get you to the top of the mountain. Snowkiting can be done for free in lots of places. Maybe that's why it is becoming so popular.

Learning to Snowkite

Beginners start with a small kite. Small kites don't catch very much wind. This means you'll move fairly slowly and won't fly off the ground. It can be dangerous to fly too high. Before they fly, beginners need to learn how to control their kites.

The kites only need a little bit of wind to work. Beginners start with light winds pulling them across the snow. They learn to control the kite and to slow down, speed up, and change direction. When they get better they can try stronger winds.

Learning to ski or snowboard might be the best way to start. Learning to sail is helpful too. In sailing you learn to control the wind. Using a snowkite is very similar to sailing. You can even go upwind by tacking like sailors do. Tacking is going side to side.

An experienced snowkiter can fly high into the air and do tricks. But it takes some practice first.

What do Snowkiters Need?

To start snowkiting, people need skis, or a snowboard, and a kite. Foil kites are best. They are completely soft. When they hit the ground, they don't break. It is easy to lift foil kites back into the air after they fall because they are so light. Snowkites look a bit like big banana skins. They come in lots of different colors. It looks like a rainbow when there are lots of snowkites flying!

Most people like to use a harness. A harness holds the kite. It gives your arms a break. There are two different harnesses. Waist harnesses are best for tricks. Sitting harnesses are good for beginners.

For safety, snowkiters need a helmet. Helmets are really important. Pads are good too. Some people wear knee pads and elbow pads. Some wear whole body padding. Ice is very hard! Falling over on the ice can really hurt.

Ice claws are another safety item. Ice claws are like sticks with a nail in the end. Frozen lakes can sometimes crack. If a snowkiter falls into the lake they can use their ice claws to pull themselves out.

Snowkiters wear skiing clothes. A jacket, snow pants, gloves, and goggles are important for staying warm. They need to be waterproof too. Remember that snow and ice are frozen water!

Places to Snowkite

Snowkiters can use ski fields, frozen lakes, or snowy mountains and hills. Lakes are the best because they are nice and smooth. Branches or poles hidden in the snow can be dangerous. Lakes don't have any hidden things! Huge flat ice-fields are great too. Hard snow and ice are easier to use than soft snow. In America there are lots of lakes and fields that freeze in winter.

Other Kite Sports

Kites can go with almost any sport. There is land, sand, and grass kiting. People stand up on paddle-boards with kites. They even use kites with special skateboards. Rollerskating with a kite looks fun too.

A Top Snowkiter

Molly Savard became the world's fastest snowkiter in 2017. She is the first woman to win a Global Speed Ranking Contest. She flew across the ice at 55.5 miles per hour. That's fast!

Molly grew up in North Conway in the United States. She loved skiing and mountain biking. She discovered snowkiting and became an instructor. Molly is also a plumber and a mountain-bike instructor. She's a busy person!

Molly loves snowkiting and wants people to stay safe when they try it. Molly had a serious injury in 2014. Snowkiting can be dangerous. Flying high through the air, going fast and doing flips are risky. Molly came back a year after her injury and won a competition.

---

13   What is the main purpose of the first paragraph?

Ⓐ   to encourage people to try snowkiting

Ⓑ   to help people imagine snowkiters

Ⓒ   to describe the history of snowkiting

Ⓓ   to show that the author has tried snowkiting

14   Read this sentence from the first paragraph.

It's like there is no gravity.

What does this sentence mainly emphasize?

Ⓐ   how high snowkiters go

Ⓑ   how fast snowkiters move

Ⓒ   how dangerous snowkiting can be

Ⓓ   how popular snowkiting has become

15   According to the passage, which group of people first tried snowkiting?

Ⓐ   kiteboarders

Ⓑ   sailors

Ⓒ   skiers

Ⓓ   snowboarders

16   In paragraph 4, the author describes how "there are worldwide snowkiting competitions." Which idea below does this detail best support?

ⓐ   Snowkiting requires a lot of physical fitness.

ⓑ   Snowkiting is still not as popular as skiing.

ⓒ   Snowkiting is popular with all types of people.

ⓓ   Snowkiting is taken seriously as a sport.

17   The author states that snowkiting is a bit like sailing. How is snowkiting most like sailing?

ⓐ   It uses wind to move.

ⓑ   It is a winter sport.

ⓒ   It requires snow.

ⓓ   It can be dangerous.

18   Which sentence from the passage is an opinion?

ⓐ   *When people snowkite, they stand on skis or on a snowboard.*

ⓑ   *They hold onto the kite.*

ⓒ   *The kite catches the wind and pulls them along.*

ⓓ   *Snowkiting is exciting and pretty easy to learn.*

19   According to the section titled "Learning to Snowkite," what is the main reason people start with a small kite?

Ⓐ   It is cheaper.

Ⓑ   It is more fun.

Ⓒ   It is easier.

Ⓓ   It is safer.

20   The title of the last section of the passage describes Molly Savard as a "top snowkiter." As it is used in the title, what does the word <u>top</u> mean?

Ⓐ   famous

Ⓑ   fastest

Ⓒ   highest

Ⓓ   leading

21   Explain why snowkiters are able to travel across flat ground while skiers are not. Use **two** details from the passage in your answer.

_____

_____

_____

_____

_____

22   List **two** reasons that snowskiing is a cheaper activity than skiing.

1: _____

_____

2: _____

_____

23   Complete the web below by listing **three** items that a snowkiter would need for safety.

```
        ┌─────────────────────────┐
        │     Safety Items a      │
        │   Snowkiter Needs       │
        └─────────────────────────┘
       ┌──────────┐  ┌──────────┐  ┌──────────┐
       │          │  │          │  │          │
       │          │  │          │  │          │
       │          │  │          │  │          │
       └──────────┘  └──────────┘  └──────────┘
```

24   Why are lakes a safer place to snowkite than a snowy mountain? Use **two** details from the passage in your answer.

_____

_____

_____

_____

_____

The Buckwheat
by Hans Christian Andersen

Very often, after a violent thunderstorm, a field of buckwheat appears blackened and singed, as if a flame of fire had passed over it. The country people say that this appearance is caused by lightning. But I will tell you what the sparrow says, and the sparrow heard it from an old willow tree which grew near a field of buckwheat, and is there still.

It is a large respected tree, though a little crippled by age. The trunk has been split, and out of the crevice grass and brambles grow. The tree bends forward slightly, and the branches hang quite down to the ground just like green hair. Corn grows in the surrounding fields, not only rye and barley, but oats, pretty oats that, when ripe, look like a number of little golden canary birds sitting on a bough. The corn has a smiling look and the heaviest and richest ears bend their heads low as if in humility.

Once there was also a field of buckwheat, and this field was exactly opposite to the old willow tree. The buckwheat did not bend like the other grain, but held its head proudly and stiffly on the stem.

"I am as valuable as any other corn," said he, "and I am much handsomer. My flowers are as beautiful as the bloom of the apple blossom, and it is a pleasure to look at us. Do you know of anything prettier than we are, you old willow tree?"

And the willow tree nodded his head, as if he would say, "Indeed I do."

But the buckwheat spread itself out with pride, and said, "Stupid tree; he is so old that grass grows out of his body."

There arose a very terrible storm. All the field flowers folded their leaves together, or bowed their little heads, while the storm passed over them, but the buckwheat stood tall in its pride. "Bend your head as we do," said the flowers.

"I have no occasion to do so," replied the buckwheat.

"Bend your head as we do," cried the ears of corn; "the angel of the storm is coming; his wings spread from the sky above to the earth beneath. He will strike you down before you can cry for mercy."

"I will not bend my head," said the buckwheat.

"Close your flowers and bend your leaves," said the old willow tree. "Do not look at the lightning when the cloud bursts; even men cannot do that. In a flash of lightning heaven opens, and we can look in; but the sight will strike even human beings blind. What then must happen to us, who only grow out of the earth, and are so inferior to them, if we venture to do so?"

"Inferior, indeed!" said the buckwheat. "Now I intend to have a peep into heaven." Proudly and boldly he looked up, while the lightning flashed across the sky as if the whole world were in flames.

When the dreadful storm had passed, the flowers and the corn raised their drooping heads in the pure still air, refreshed by the rain, but the buckwheat lay like a weed in the field, burnt to blackness by the lightning.

The branches of the old willow tree rustled in the wind, and large water drops fell from his green leaves as if the old willow were weeping. Then the sparrows asked why he was weeping, when all around him seemed so cheerful.

"See," they said, "how the sun shines, and the clouds float in the blue sky. Do you not smell the sweet perfume from flower and bush? Wherefore do you weep, old willow tree?"

Then the willow told them of the haughty pride of the buckwheat, and of the punishment which followed.

25   What is the main purpose of the first paragraph?

   Ⓐ   to introduce the main theme of the passage

   Ⓑ   to describe what the passage is going to explain

   Ⓒ   to show that the events never really happened

   Ⓓ   to make the reader care about the buckwheat

26   Which phrase from the first paragraph is an example of alliteration?

   Ⓐ   *violent thunderstorm*

   Ⓑ   *blackened and singed*

   Ⓒ   *flame of fire*

   Ⓓ   *old willow tree*

27   Which detail from the first paragraph describes an event that could not really happen?

   Ⓐ   A violent thunderstorm occurs.

   Ⓑ   People think damage from a thunderstorm is caused by lightning.

   Ⓒ   A sparrow hears a story from a willow tree.

   Ⓓ   A willow tree grows near a field of buckwheat.

28 How does the buckwheat's dialogue in paragraph 4 make it seem?

Ⓐ boastful

Ⓑ brave

Ⓒ gentle

Ⓓ selfish

29 Based on your answer to Question 28, list **two** details from paragraph 4 that support your answer.

1: _____

_____

2: _____

_____

30 What is the most likely reason the flowers tell the buckwheat to "bend your head as we do"?

Ⓐ They are jealous of the buckwheat.

Ⓑ They are scared of the buckwheat.

Ⓒ They are worried about the buckwheat.

Ⓓ They are making fun of the buckwheat.

31   Read this sentence from the passage.

Proudly and boldly he looked up, while the lightning flashed across the sky as if the whole world were in flames.

Which part of the sentence uses exaggeration?

Ⓐ   *Proudly and boldly he looked up*

Ⓑ   *while the lightning flashed*

Ⓒ   *across the sky*

Ⓓ   *as if the whole world were in flames*

32   What does the willow's reaction to the buckwheat being burned show about him?

Ⓐ   He feels sorry for the buckwheat.

Ⓑ   He fears he will be punished for what has happened.

Ⓒ   He is proud of the buckwheat for being brave.

Ⓓ   He thinks the buckwheat deserved to be punished.

33   The theme of the passage is mostly about the importance of being –

Ⓐ   determined

Ⓑ   humble

Ⓒ   peaceful

Ⓓ   respectful

34   Complete the web below by listing **three** details the author gives in the second paragraph to support the idea that the willow tree is "crippled by age."

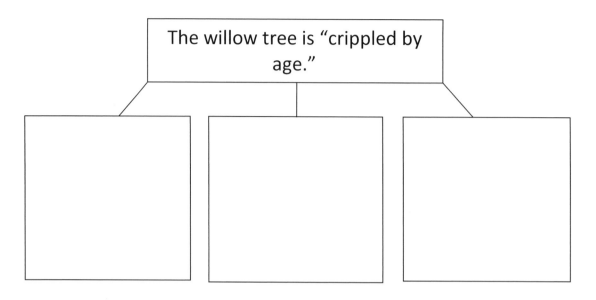

The willow tree is "crippled by age."

35   The old willow tree warns the buckwheat not to look at the lightning. Explain how this warning makes the buckwheat more determined to look at the lightning. Use **two** details from the passage in your answer.

_____

_____

_____

_____

_____

36   Compare what the corn does during the storm to what the buckwheat does. How does this affect what happens to each during the storm? Use **two** details from the passage in your answer.

_____

_____

_____

_____

_____

_____

_____

_____

_____

_____

_____

_____

_____

_____

_____

_____

End-of-Grade Reading

Practice Test 3

Session 2

Instructions

Read each passage and answer the questions that follow it.

For each multiple-choice question, fill in the circle for the correct answer. For other types of questions, follow the instructions given. Some of the questions require a written answer. Write your answer on the lines provided.

The students at Avoca Elementary School were asked to conduct a science experiment and write a report. Jon wrote the report below to show his findings on plant growth and sunlight.

Experiment: Sunlight on Plant Growth

My experiment was to show if plants need sunlight to grow. First, I planted one bean seedling in each of the three pots. The three seedlings were all the same size. I watered the plants at the same time every day for three weeks. I gave each plant the same amount of water.

One plant was placed in a dark closet with no light. Another plant was placed in a bedroom that had a little sunlight. There was one large window that faced the south side of the house. I closed the blinds part way during the daytime. The third plant was placed near a living room window that did not have blinds or a curtain. This plant received full sun all day long.

Every day when I watered the plants, I measured their height with a ruler. I also marked down the color of the leaves of the bean plants. In addition, I observed the growth of the stems. After three weeks, I summarized the findings. I will share these results.

The bean plant that was placed by the open window grew the most. Its leaves were the largest. Its stems were wide and strong and the plant's leaves were bright green and healthy. The plant placed in the bedroom with a little light grew about half the size of the first plant. Its leaves were light green and medium size. The stems were narrower than the first plant. The plant that was in the dark closet grew the least. The leaves were small and had yellow tips with brown edges. Its stems were quite skinny and weak.

I learned from this experiment that sunlight affects how bean plants grow. Plants get their energy from sunlight. This is called photosynthesis. This means that the light is turned into food for the plants.

As has been seen, bean plants grow and change with the amount of light they receive. They grow in size, thickness, and structure. They turn different colors. If there is less light, photosynthesis slows down. Then the green color disappears and the leaves turn a lighter green, yellow, and even brown. The stems don't grow as well either.

I learned a clear lesson from the experiment. I now understand the importance of sunlight on plant growth. Plants, like all living things, need energy to grow. The more sunlight a plant receives, the larger it will grow.

Photosynthesis

The process of turning light energy into chemical energy is called photosynthesis. The process of photosynthesis is how plants get their energy.

Plant leaves and stems have a high amount of a green pigment named chlorophyll contained in them. Light energy from the sun is absorbed by the chlorophyll. This energy is used to power a reaction between water and carbon dioxide. This reaction produces glucose and oxygen. The plant stores the glucose and uses it for energy. The oxygen is released into the air.

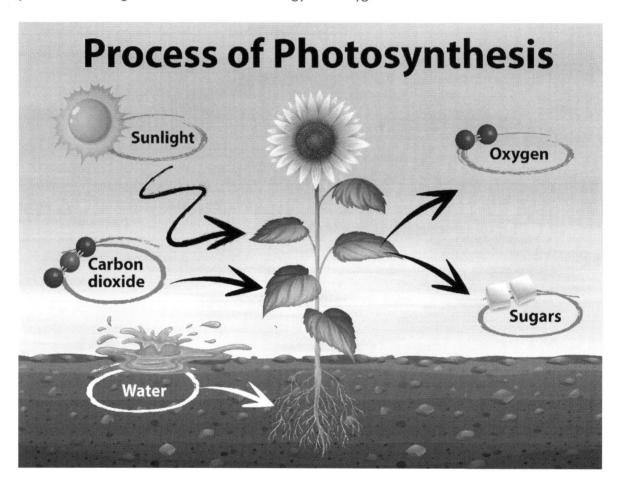

37   Which of these was different about how the three bean plants were treated?

    Ⓐ   how much water they were given

    Ⓑ   how often they were watered

    Ⓒ   how much light they received

    Ⓓ   how often they were placed outside

38   Which phrase best describes how paragraph 2 is organized?

    Ⓐ   order of events

    Ⓑ   compare and contrast

    Ⓒ   problem and solution

    Ⓓ   cause and effect

39   Which of these did Jon observe and record for the plants?

    Ⓐ   the number of leaves

    Ⓑ   the length of the leaves

    Ⓒ   the color of the leaves

    Ⓓ   the thickness of the leaves

40 Which paragraph has the main purpose of showing how the plants were different after three weeks?

Ⓐ Paragraph 2

Ⓑ Paragraph 3

Ⓒ Paragraph 4

Ⓓ Paragraph 5

41 Jon describes how he measured the heights of the three plants with a ruler. Which of these would NOT be a suitable way of summarizing this data?

Ⓐ chart

Ⓑ graph

Ⓒ map

Ⓓ table

42 Read these sentences from the passage.

Plants get their energy from sunlight. This is called photosynthesis.

The word <u>photosynthesis</u> contains the Greek root <u>photo</u>. What does the Greek root <u>photo</u> mean?

Ⓐ earth

Ⓑ light

Ⓒ plant

Ⓓ water

43   According to the passage, what is chlorophyll?

Ⓐ   a chemical reaction

Ⓑ   a form of sunlight

Ⓒ   a type of plant

Ⓓ   a green pigment

44   How is the information in the section titled "Photosynthesis" related to Jon's report?

Ⓐ   It shows that plants also need plenty of water to grow well.

Ⓑ   It shows the different roles of each part of a plant.

Ⓒ   It explains why plants grow larger with more sunlight.

Ⓓ   It explains why plants that grow well have green leaves.

45   Based on the diagram, which part of a plant takes in water?

Ⓐ   flower

Ⓑ   leaves

Ⓒ   roots

Ⓓ   stem

46   Complete the summary of photosynthesis below by writing the words listed in the correct places.

carbon dioxide   oxygen   sunlight

sugars   water

Photosynthesis

Plants Take In   **Plants Release**

47   Complete the table below to summarize what the leaves looked like on each plant in Jon's experiment.

	Plant in Dark Closet	Plant in Bedroom	Plant in Full Sun
Leaf size	small		
Leaf color	yellow tips with brown edges		

48   How were the stems of the plant in the dark closet different from the stems of the plant in full sun? Use **two** details from the passage in your answer.

_____

_____

_____

_____

_____

All About Kittens

Maria loved animals. Every day, she would check out a library book about an animal she wanted to learn more about. Yesterday, she read about wild horses and what they eat. Today, she wanted to learn about cats.

Before this morning, Maria thought she knew a lot about cats. She knew that they liked fish and chicken. But, she did not know where they liked to sleep or what they liked to play with. She also did not know what kittens liked to eat, and Maria thought this was very important to know.

Maria visited the library in the morning, before school started. She used the computer to see what cat or kitten books were ready for checkout, but she did not find any. She decided to ask the teacher.

"Mrs. Jones?" Maria asked quietly.

"Yes, my dear?" Mrs. Jones said.

"I am looking for a book about cats or kittens," Maria said.

"Oh!" Mrs. Jones said with surprise. "Let me check, dear." Mrs. Jones used her computer to look up what books the library had about cats and kittens. Her computer would show the books that were checked out and when they were due back.

"Thank you," Maria said.

"It is my pleasure, Maria," Mrs. Jones began. "It looks like most of our books about cats and kittens are checked out until next week. One about caring for kittens should be returned today. Will that work?"

"Yes!" Maria shouted. Mrs. Jones put her pointer finger to her lips.

"Shh," Mrs. Jones said. "Come by at lunch and see if it's been returned."

Maria nodded.

At lunch, Maria asked her teacher, Ms. Smith, if she could go to the library after she was done eating. Ms. Smith said she could go during the last ten minutes of lunch. Ms. Smith also asked Maria why she needed a book about caring for kittens.

Maria told Ms. Smith that her mother said that she could get a kitten if she knew how to take care of it. Maria needed to learn what kittens needed to eat, when they needed to sleep, and what toys they should play with. Ms. Smith smiled and nodded.

At the library, Mrs. Jones told Maria that the book had not been returned yet. She gave Maria a note to give to Ms. Smith to let her come back at the end of the day before she got on the school bus.

When it was almost the end of the day, Maria started to worry. She wanted to make sure she got the book about kittens today because her neighbor's cat had just had a litter of kittens. Her mother said she could keep one if she learned how to take care of it. She had picked out the orange one with brown stripes on its legs.

The kittens were almost ready to move into their new homes and Maria had not learned how to take care of kittens. Her mother had reminded her about their deal just that morning.

When Maria got to the library, Mrs. Jones did not look happy.

"Sorry Maria, the book was not returned on time," Mrs. Jones said with a frown. "Be sure to check back tomorrow!" Maria knew that by tomorrow it might be too late. The orange kitten would likely be gone.

Maria got on her bus and sat quietly the entire ride home. She frowned while she looked out the window. She saw that many yards had dogs and many windows had cats. She knew when she got home, she would only find her goldfish, Barry.

When the bus stopped at her road, Maria got off the bus. She walked slowly to her house, trying to figure out what she was going to tell her mother. Maria and her mother had already agreed on a name for the orange kitten. Since the kitten was a female and she was orange, they would call her Ginger.

Maria got to her house and unlocked the door. Her mother was in the kitchen, making her favorite afterschool snack. She was making grilled peanut butter, banana, and jelly sandwiches. This would put her in a better mood until she had to tell her mother the truth.

Maria put her backpack on the table and sat down quietly.

"Hi Maria, how was school?" her mother asked.

"I did not learn about kittens," Maria said, sounding upset.

"What?" her mother asked.

"You said if I wanted to keep Ginger, I had to learn about how to take care of a kitten. I forgot until this morning and the library did not have a book about it. Now we can't keep Ginger," Maria said. Maria's mother laughed softly and looked at the picnic basket on the table.

Maria had been so upset when she came in, she had not noticed it before. She wondered if her mother was taking her on a picnic today.

"Look in the basket Maria," her mother said. Maria wanted to see what snacks her mother had packed for their picnic and opened the basket right away.

Inside, she found a little orange kitten, sleeping in a ball, and purring happily. A tiny collar was around its neck, with a golden tag with 'Ginger' written on it.

"You should also check your room," Maria's mother added. "There's a pile of books about kittens I borrowed from the school library for you."

"Mom," Maria laughed. "That's why I couldn't find any books today. You borrowed them all!"

49   What does the photograph at the start of the passage mainly show?

Ⓐ   how much Maria loves animals

Ⓑ   why Maria wants to learn about animals

Ⓒ   what type of animal Maria wants to have

Ⓓ   where Maria goes to learn about animals

50   Read this sentence from the passage.

Maria told Ms. Smith that her mother said that she could get a kitten if she knew how to take care of it.

Why is this sentence important in the passage?

Ⓐ   It tells what type of book Maria needs to find.

Ⓑ   It shows that Maria cannot keep a secret.

Ⓒ   It explains why getting the book is important to Maria.

Ⓓ   It warns that Maria is not ready to take care of a pet.

51   Read this sentence from the passage.

Her mother had reminded her about their deal just that morning.

Which word means about the same as deal?

Ⓐ   agreement

Ⓑ   discussion

Ⓒ   fight

Ⓓ   problem

52   How does Maria feel during the bus ride home after school?

Ⓐ   angry

Ⓑ   confused

Ⓒ   lonely

Ⓓ   sad

53   Based on your answer to Question 52, which statement best explains why Maria feels that way?

Ⓐ   She does not understand why the person did not return the book on time.

Ⓑ   She does not feel like the deal she made with her mother was fair.

Ⓒ   She does not think she is going to be allowed to get the kitten.

Ⓓ   She does not know how she is going to be able to look after the kitten.

54   Read this sentence from the passage.

She walked slowly to her house, trying to figure out what she was going to tell her mother.

Which word could best replace "walked slowly" to show that Maria is upset?

Ⓐ   hiked

Ⓑ   plodded

Ⓒ   raced

Ⓓ   strolled

55 Read these sentences from the passage.

> **"You said if I wanted to keep Ginger, I had to learn about how to take care of a kitten. I forgot until this morning and the library did not have a book about it. Now we can't keep Ginger," Maria said. Maria's mother laughed softly and looked at the picnic basket on the table.**

Why does Maria's mother laugh?

Ⓐ   She feels sorry for Maria and wants to cheer her up.

Ⓑ   She thinks that Maria has not earned the kitten.

Ⓒ   She knows that Maria is about to get the kitten.

Ⓓ   She worries that Maria will not take care of the kitten.

56 Which detail best supports the idea that Maria already cares about the kitten a lot?

Ⓐ   The kitten is from her neighbor's cat.

Ⓑ   The kitten has brown stripes on its legs.

Ⓒ   Maria has given the kitten a name.

Ⓓ   Maria has made a bed for the kitten.

57 Complete the web below by listing **three** things that Maria wants to learn about kittens.

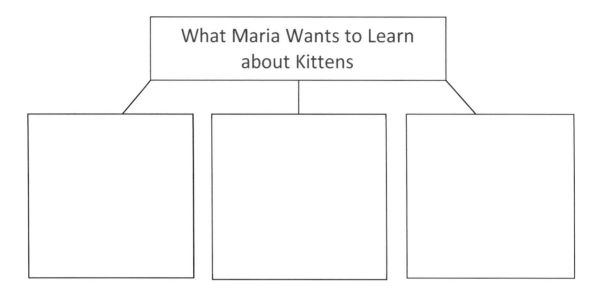

58 The author describes how Maria keeps going back to the library to see if the book on kittens is available. What does this mainly create in the passage?

Ⓐ   confusion

Ⓑ   excitement

Ⓒ   humor

Ⓓ   suspense

59   How do you think Maria feels when she opens the picnic basket? Use **two** details from the passage to support your answer.

_____

_____

_____

_____

_____

60   Do you think Maria will take good care of the kitten? Explain why you feel that way.

_____

_____

_____

_____

_____

Directions: This set has two passages in it. Read each passage and answer the questions that follow it. Then use both passages to answer the final question.

How to Care for Your New Pet Puppy

Once you have brought your new puppy home, there is a lot to do. If you do these things, you and your puppy will both be happy.

Firstly, you need to prepare your house for the puppy. You don't want it to get hurt or break anything. Put away any breakable items. Put away any dangerous chemicals or cleaning products. Also, a tall trash can would be a good idea. This will prevent your puppy from knocking it over and making a terrible mess.

Your puppy will need a bed. Prepare a bed that is dry, soft, and warm. Give your new puppy a blanket to snuggle under. At night, it might be good to make a puppy house near your bed. If it is near your bed, you can hear it get up when it wants to go to the toilet.

Your puppy will need a good supply of food and water. Buy at least two bowls. One bowl will be for food and the other will be for water. Remember to buy nutritious food for your puppy. If you need help selecting the right food, talk to your vet or your parents. Don't forget about treats either. Treats help with training and may also be good for their teeth.

Puppies also love toys to play with. It gives them something to chew on. It also stops the puppy from becoming bored. When puppies become bored, they can start to be naughty. They might tear up pillows and cushions, chew shoes, or scratch at carpets and curtains. It is much better for everyone if a puppy has good toys to play with and chew! Buy a range of toys and make sure you play with your puppy often.

When playing with your puppy, be careful and make sure your puppy is not overwhelmed. Some puppies like rough play, but others might be scared at first. A loud toy or a bouncy ball could even scare a puppy that is not used to these things. Remember that everything is new to the puppy. They have not been with you long and they are living in a new place. Puppies can become stressed by new things. Be watchful of your puppy and give it time to rest if it seems to be stressed. Remember that a stressed puppy might even start to bite. This is the puppy's way of protecting itself.

Regularly bath your puppy. Bathing your puppy can help prevent fleas and other health problems. You may also like to buy some puppy care tools such as a brush and nail clippers. Some dogs can be harder to groom than others. If you don't want to do it yourself, you can call a service that will come to your home to wash your dog and to do professional grooming.

Always remember to comfort your puppy by patting it softly. This will help you to bond with your puppy and it will feel loved. Also, because they are little and fragile and can be hurt easily, remember to handle your puppy with care.

It is important that your puppy gets enough exercise. Remember to walk your puppy every day. Buy a harness and a lead as soon as you can and start by walking your puppy around the house. Then walk it around the block and then the neighborhood. Puppies love to roam and it is also good for their health.

However, it is also important to be careful when you are out and about with your puppy. You should keep it on the lead at all times. You might think it is safe, but puppies can become curious and run off. You could lose your puppy or it could even run onto the road. You also want to keep your puppy safe from other larger dogs.

61   Based on the information in the second paragraph, summarize the **three** things you should put away to keep a puppy safe.

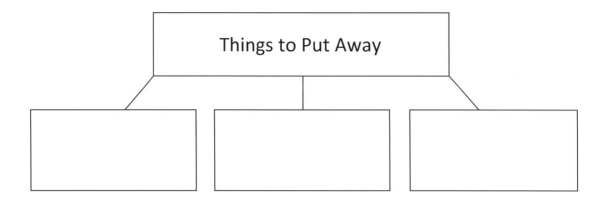

62   Read this sentence from the passage.

Remember to buy nutritious food for your puppy.

What does the word <u>nutritious</u> mean?

Ⓐ   expensive

Ⓑ   fresh

Ⓒ   healthy

Ⓓ   tasty

63   Read this sentence from the passage.

Also, because they are little and fragile and can be hurt easily, remember to handle your puppy with care.

The main message of this sentence is that you should be –

Ⓐ   friendly

Ⓑ   gentle

Ⓒ   patient

Ⓓ   quiet

64   What does the photograph at the end of the passage mainly represent?

Ⓐ   a puppy being groomed well

Ⓑ   a puppy getting enough exercise

Ⓒ   a puppy feeling safe and loved

Ⓓ   a puppy having toys to play with

65   How can toys stop puppies from doing damage to a home? Use **two** details from the passage in your answer.

_____

_____

_____

_____

66   List **two** problems that could occur if you don't keep a puppy on a leash when going for a walk.

1: _____

_____

2: _____

_____

The Body Language of Dogs

Dogs can't talk to tell you how they are feeling. However, dogs are very good at showing how they are feeling. You can observe a dog and know if it is feeling happy and calm, or stressed and fearful. It is important to understand how your dog is feeling. If you can see that your dog is stressed, you can take action to make it feel better. Maybe it is scared of all the noise in a busy place or frightened of another dog. Maybe it has been inside too long and is feeling bored. Once you see that your dog is worried or stressed, try to work out why and then take action. This can calm your dog and prevent it from becoming so stressed that it will start barking, or even biting.

Dog Body Language

Happy

Relaxed posture, mouth open, wagging tail.

Dog is friendly and invites interactions.

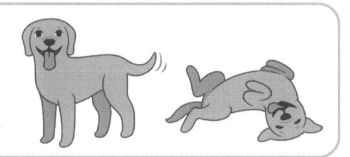

Worried

Dog avoids eye contact, body tense, tail low. Licks its lips or yawns.

Lifting front paw in hopes of disengaging.

Very stressed

Very tense, cowering and trembling or growls and snarls, baring its teeth.

It is threatened and will bite if it must!

67   What is the main purpose of the first paragraph?

   Ⓐ   to explain how to tell how your dog is feeling

   Ⓑ   to explain why it is important to know how your dog is feeling

   Ⓒ   to explain that dogs have different feelings

   Ⓓ   to explain how to make your dog feel happy

68   Read these sentences from the passage.

> **Maybe it is scared of all the noise in a busy place or frightened of another dog. Maybe it has been inside too long and is feeling bored.**

Which word best describes these sentences?

   Ⓐ   examples

   Ⓑ   facts

   Ⓒ   opinions

   Ⓓ   solutions

69   Select **all** the actions that are those of a dog that is worried.

   ☐   bares its teeth

   ☐   growls

   ☐   licks its lips

   ☐   snarls

   ☐   wags its tail

   ☐   yawns

70   Which word from the poster titled "Dog Body Language" means the same as <u>shaking</u>?

    Ⓐ   baring

    Ⓑ   cowering

    Ⓒ   trembling

    Ⓓ   wagging

71   Describe **two** details you can see in the illustrations of a very stressed dog that show that the dog is stressed.

1: _____

_____

2: _____

_____

72   Why is it important to be able to tell that a dog is very stressed? Use details from the passage to support your answer.

_____

_____

_____

_____

_____

Directions: Use both passages to answer the following question.

73   How could the information in "The Body Language of Dogs" help you play with a puppy in a suitable way? Use details from both passages in your answer.

_____

_____

_____

_____

_____

_____

_____

_____

_____

_____

_____

_____

_____

_____

_____

End-of-Grade Reading

Practice Test 4

Session 1

Instructions

Read each passage and answer the questions that follow it.

For each multiple-choice question, fill in the circle for the correct answer. For other types of questions, follow the instructions given. Some of the questions require a written answer. Write your answer on the lines provided.

Monument Valley

The Monument Valley Navajo Tribal Park is a famous tourist attraction. It is famous because of its beauty and its use in many films and advertisements. It is a well-known icon of the American Southwest. Many people visit Monument Valley Navajo Tribal Park every year to spend time there and take photographs of the area.

Monument Valley Navajo Tribal Park is located on the border region of Utah and Arizona. It lies within a Navajo Indian Reservation. The Navajo Nation is one of the largest American Indian tribes. Therefore, the entire park is a very culturally rich region.

There is one main road that runs through the area (US 163). This road links Kayenta, Arizona, with the US 191 in Utah. This road allows visitors to easily access the region.

Monument Valley Navajo Tribal Park is characterized by large rock formations and red, sandy plains. The rock formations are known as buttes. They are made of sandstone and are typically between 400 and 1000 feet tall. Some of the famous formations are the Mitten Buttes, the Three Sisters, Yei-bi-chai, North Window, Merrick Butte and Totem Pole. There are many other buttes and landmarks to see.

There is a small settlement in the Navajo Indian Reservation known as Goulding. If you plan to visit the area, there is accommodation available at Goulding. There is also accommodation available at Kayenta.

Things to Do

There is a lot of sightseeing to be done in the Monument Valley Navajo Tribal Park. There are tours available to visitors. Many people do self-guided tours, but a guided tour is a good option because the tour guides can provide details about the area. There are also Jeep tours which are quite popular with visitors.

If you enjoy hiking, then the Wildcat Trail is for you. It is a four-mile loop that offers close-up views of many famous monuments. If you prefer to get around Monument Valley Navajo Tribal Park on foot, this is the only self-guided trail in the park.

Most of the park's best attractions can be seen from Valley Drive. Valley Drive is a seventeen-mile dirt road that leaves from the visitor center. The road is suitable for most cars; however, some choose to hire a four-wheel drive. The Valley Drive tour takes about two hours. On the Valley Drive, it is advised that you stay in the vehicle. Leaving the trail and wandering around is not permitted.

Monument Valley's striking beauty makes it popular with photographers and artists.

Many also enjoy other activities such as stargazing. The beautiful clear nights make Monument Valley Navajo Tribal Park a great place to view the stars at night. Don't forget to wake up early and watch the magnificent sunrise. The surroundings are peaceful. This makes watching the sunrise very relaxing and enjoyable.

There are many other services and facilities for tourists in the area. You can enjoy American and Native American cuisine at local restaurants. They love welcoming visitors from all over America and the world. In and around the park, there are also Navajo vendors selling arts, crafts and other items. These would make excellent gifts for family and friends.

Geography and Climate

Monument Valley Navajo Tribal Park is 5,200 feet above sea level. It is in the south-east portion of the Great Basin Desert and about in the middle of the Colorado Plateau. The entire park covers an area of approximately 92,000 acres.

The region is classified as having a desert climate. However, there are seasonal rains and snowfall. In fact, in winter, it can be very cold and snowy. The highest snowfall typically occurs in the months of December and January. If you are visiting in winter, be sur

e to pack lots of warm clothes.

The summertime, on the other hand, is warm. Temperatures average in the 90s (°F). The warmest temperatures typically occur in June, July and August. If you prefer the warmer weather, this is a good time to visit the park.

The Surrounding Areas

There are also many famous tourist attractions in the area around Monument Valley Navajo Tribal Park. These too offer spectacular views and many other sightseeing opportunities.

Mexican Hut, Utah, is about 20 miles north-east of the park. Mexican Hut is a small town that was established many years ago during a small mining boom. Like Monument Valley Navajo Tribal Park, it is visited by many tourists every year. In Mexican Hut, companies offer river and overland tours of the surrounding wilderness areas. There are many rugged rock formations for those who enjoy rock climbing.

There are also many famous scenic byways in the area. A well-known byway is known as the Trail of the Ancients. Along this byway, there are many interesting archaeological and cultural attractions. For example, there is the Four Corners Monument and the Edge of the Cedars State Park and Museum.

Conclusion

It is easy to see why Monument Valley is a famous tourist attraction. With its magnificent rock formations, red sand, and clear nights it is a truly magical place. Many people travel to the area to enjoy the things the park has to offer. I suggest you pay a visit there too.

The Four Corners Monument is a site where four states meet. Yes, you can stand in four states all at the same time! It's a popular spot to take fun photos.

1   Read this sentence from the passage.

It is a well-known icon of the American Southwest.

Which word means about the same as <u>icon</u>?

Ⓐ   idea

Ⓑ   memory

Ⓒ   plan

Ⓓ   symbol

2   What is the main purpose of the passage overall?

Ⓐ   to persuade people to visit Monument Valley

Ⓑ   to explain how to get to Monument Valley

Ⓒ   to teach people about the history of Monument Valley

Ⓓ   to encourage people to respect and look after Monument Valley

3   Which sentence from the passage would make the best caption for the photograph in the first section?

Ⓐ   *It is famous because of its beauty and its use in many films and advertisements.*

Ⓑ   *Monument Valley Navajo Tribal Park is located on the border region of Utah and Arizona.*

Ⓒ   *Monument Valley Navajo Tribal Park is characterized by large rock formations and red, sandy plains.*

Ⓓ   *There is a small settlement in the Navajo Indian Reservation known as Goulding.*

4   Read this sentence from the passage.

> **Monument Valley Navajo Tribal Park is located on the border region of Utah and Arizona.**

Which of these would be best to add to the passage to represent this detail?

Ⓐ   graph

Ⓑ   map

Ⓒ   table

Ⓓ   timeline

5   Which two paragraphs from the first section of the paragraph mainly give practical information to help visitors to the area? Select the **two** best answers.

☐   Paragraph 1

☐   Paragraph 2

☐   Paragraph 3

☐   Paragraph 4

☐   Paragraph 5

6   The passage gives the names of six famous formations in Monument Valley. Which formation mentioned is most likely the one shown in the photograph at the bottom of the first page? Select the **one** best answer.

☐   Mitten Buttes

☐   Three Sisters

☐   Yei-bi-chai

☐   North Window

☐   Merrick Butte

☐   Totem Pole

7   Based on the passage, why is a guided tour better than a self-guided tour?

Ⓐ   Visitors are able to learn more.

Ⓑ   Visitors are safer and do not risk getting lost.

Ⓒ   Visitors are taken to the most important sites.

Ⓓ   Visitors are likely to enjoy sharing the experience.

8   Which sentence from the passage is an opinion?

Ⓐ   *There are many other services and facilities for tourists in the area.*

Ⓑ   *You can enjoy American and Native American cuisine at local restaurants.*

Ⓒ   *In and around the park, there are also Navajo vendors selling arts, crafts and other items.*

Ⓓ   *These would make excellent gifts for family and friends.*

9 Complete the web below by listing **three** outdoor activities popular in Monument Valley.

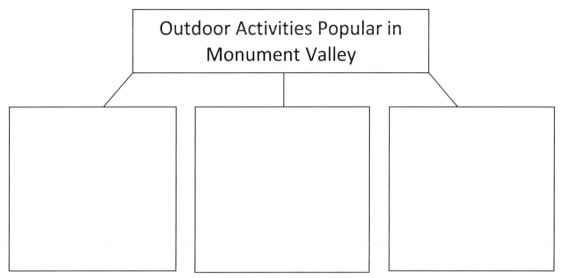

10 Describe **two** differences between the Wildcat Trail and the Valley Drive.

1: _____

_____

2: _____

_____

11 In the section titled "Surrounding Areas," the author describes Mexican Hut. How are the activities at Mexican Hut similar to the activities at Monument Valley? Use **two** details from the passage in your answer.

_____

_____

_____

_____

_____

12 The author describes Monument Valley as a "truly magical place." Do you think it sounds like a magical place? Explain why you feel that way.

_____

_____

_____

_____

_____

Introduction

A dike is a wall built to stop water flooding onto land. Holland is mostly flat and water can easily flow from the sea or rivers and flood the lands. Dikes are built along the edges of land to stop this flow of water. In this play set in Holland, Peter discovers a hole in the dike.

The Hole in the Dike

SCENE I

TIME: *late afternoon in autumn*
PLACE: *Holland*

[*The* CHILDREN *enter. They carry buckets full of nuts.*]

GRETCHEN: How cold it is!

FRIEDA: Let us run. Then we shall not be cold.

PETER: How can we run? We shall spill our nuts.

FRIEDA: We are so far from home!

JACOB: We went so far to find the nuts.

GRETCHEN: It will soon be dark.

FRIEDA: We must walk as fast as we can.

GRETCHEN: Why do you stop, Peter?

PETER: There is water on the sand here.

JACOB: Come, Peter, come!

PETER: Where has this water come from?

FRIEDA: Come, come, Peter!

PETER: There was no rain yesterday. There was no rain today.

GRETCHEN: Come, Peter!

PETER: What if the water comes through the dike!

JACOB: Oh, that could not be! How could water get through that thick wall?

PETER: There might be a hole in it. I will see.

GRETCHEN: Peter, Peter! Your mother waits for you.

PETER: I must find where the water comes from.

GRETCHEN: Well, I will not wait.

JACOB: Nor I!

FRIEDA: Nor I! It is too cold.

[*They go. Peter runs to the dike and looks at it carefully.*]

PETER: Ah, I thought so! Here is a little hole! The water comes through it from the sea. Soon the hole will be larger. I must find stones and fill it. (*He looks about for stones.*) Dear me! Dear me! I cannot find a single stone! What shall I do? The hole will grow larger and larger. The sea will come in and cover all the land. What shall I do? I cannot go and tell the people. That would take too long. What shall I do? What shall I do? (*He thinks for a moment.*) I know! I know how to stop it! (*He thrusts his arm through the hole. He shivers.*) How cold it is!

SCENE II

TIME: *the next morning*
PLACE: *the street near Peter's home*

[*The* MOTHER *stands in the door of her home looking up and down the street.*]

MOTHER: He does not come! Well, I will go to Jacob's after him. I must teach him that he cannot stay away all night. I will punish him for what he has done.

[*Enter the* PRINCE, SOLDIERS, *and* PEOPLE. *Four soldiers carry* PETER *on their shoulders.*]

A SOLDIER: Hurrah for Peter!

A MAN: Hurrah for Peter!

SOLDIERS: Hurrah! Hurrah!

PEOPLE: Hurrah! Hurrah!

MOTHER: What is this? Why do you carry Peter?

PRINCE: Peter has saved us!

MOTHER: What do you mean?

PRINCE: He put his arm in a hole in the dike. All night long he stood there! All night long he kept out the sea! We found him there this morning. Poor little boy, he was so cold!

MOTHER: Ah, my Peter! My dear Peter!

PRINCE: He is a brave boy. The king wants to see him and to thank him. Come, soldiers, to the king with Peter! Come, to the king! To the king!

[*They go with Peter on their shoulders.*]

SOLDIERS: Hurrah for Peter!

PEOPLE: Hurrah for Peter!

13   What is the main purpose of the introduction at the start of the passage?

Ⓐ   to explain why the play was written

Ⓑ   to help readers understand the message of the play

Ⓒ   to summarize the main events of the play

Ⓓ   to give background information on the setting of the play

14   At the start of the play, why were the children far from home?

Ⓐ   They were going for a swim.

Ⓑ   They were collecting nuts.

Ⓒ   They were checking the dike.

Ⓓ   They were racing each other.

15   Which line at the start of the play gives details about the time the events are taking place?

Ⓐ   *FRIEDA: We are so far from home!*

Ⓑ   *JACOB: We went so far to find the nuts.*

Ⓒ   *GRETCHEN: It will soon be dark.*

Ⓓ   *FRIEDA: We must walk as fast as we can.*

16   Read this line from the play.

PETER: Where has this water come from?

How would Peter most likely sound when saying this line?

Ⓐ   angry

Ⓑ   curious

Ⓒ   excited

Ⓓ   sad

17   Which line best shows that Peter is determined? Select the **one** line that best shows that Peter is determined.

☐   *PETER: There is water on the sand here.*

☐   *PETER: Where has this water come from?*

☐   *PETER: There was no rain yesterday. There was no rain today.*

☐   *PETER: What if the water comes through the dike!*

☐   *PETER: There might be a hole in it. I will see.*

☐   *PETER: I must find where the water comes from.*

18   Read these lines from the play.

> **PETER: Ah, I thought so! Here is a little hole! The water comes through it from the sea. Soon the hole will be larger. I must find stones and fill it. (*He looks about for stones.*) Dear me! Dear me! I cannot find a single stone! What shall I do? The hole will grow larger and larger. The sea will come in and cover all the land. What shall I do? I cannot go and tell the people. That would take too long. What shall I do? What shall I do? (*He thinks for a moment.*) I know! I know how to stop it! (*He thrusts his arm through the hole. He shivers.*) How cold it is!**

What do the sentences in italics tell?

Ⓐ   how Peter is feeling

Ⓑ   how Peter is speaking

Ⓒ   actions that Peter is taking

Ⓓ   thoughts that Peter has

19   When Peter is trying to work out how to stop the leak, he keeps repeating the phrase "what shall I do?" What does this mainly suggest about how Peter feels?

Ⓐ   He is starting to panic.

Ⓑ   He wishes his friends had stayed.

Ⓒ   He thinks he is going to get into trouble.

Ⓓ   He is too cold to think clearly.

20   What does the photograph near the end of the passage mainly emphasize?

Ⓐ   how determined Peter felt

Ⓑ   how cold Peter was

Ⓒ   how long Peter stayed out for

Ⓓ   how upset Peter's mother was

21 In Scene I, do the other children care about the water on the sand? Use **two** details from the play to support your answer.

_____

_____

_____

_____

_____

22 The table below lists two actions Peter thinks about taking when he finds the hole. Complete the table by writing the reason why Peter does not take the action.

Action Peter Considers	Why Peter Does Not Take the Action
filling the hole with stones	
going to tell the people	

23   At the start of Scene II, Peter's mother is mad at him for staying away all night. Do you think she would still be mad at the end of the play? Explain your answer.

_____

_____

_____

_____

_____

24   Describe **two** ways that Peter is praised and rewarded for blocking the hole in the dike.

1: _____

_____

2: _____

_____

I Don't Want to Wear a Uniform

February 4, 2020

Dear Principal Sanchez,

I think that we should not wear uniforms. Every day we have to wear the same clothing, and it is boring. I do not want to wear the same thing every day because I want to wear my own clothes. My clothes make me feel good about myself. I also know my friends want to wear their favorite shirts and jeans. The uniform makes us all look the same, and that doesn't help us. We want to express ourselves through our clothing.

I promise that I won't wear clothing with bad words or holes. I will make sure that everything I wear is appropriate for school. I just want to wear things that I like. You can still make rules about what we can wear, and we will be sure to respect and follow those rules. My friends and I want to wear t-shirts, jeans, hoodies, and even dresses or skirts to school. We also want to be allowed to wear shorts in the warmer weather.

I want to wear clothing that is comfortable so I can focus in school. I also don't like the uniform because it is itchy. I hate to wear the wool skirt in the winter, and it always slides around my stomach. In the winter, I want to wear jeans, because my legs are cold when I walk to school. The other girls in my class agree with me. They don't like the skirt either.

I talked to the boys also. They said they don't like their shirts or their pants. The shirts aren't very comfortable, and the pants get too hot. The boys said they do not like the school rule about uniforms. Both the girls and boys at our school want to wear their own clothing. If we wear our clothing we won't say bad things about the uniform anymore.

My mother also says that the uniforms are expensive and she cannot afford to buy me another skirt. I have to wear the same skirt all week and wash it every evening. My mom gets mad at me whenever the skirt gets dirty, but it's hard to get through the whole day without getting it a little dirty. I can save my mom money if I don't have to wear a uniform anymore.

Overall, I think all the students will be happy if there is no rule about uniforms. We can write new rules about a dress code and you can read them and agree to them. We just want to be comfortable and warm. We also want to wear our favorite things and feel good about ourselves. Taking away the rules about wearing uniforms will be great for everyone, and I hope you will consider it.

Thank you for your time.

Sincerely,

Rose Camille

We get tired of wearing the same thing every single day!

We'll be happier when we can wear comfortable clothing that suits us!

25   Which of these is the greeting of the letter?

    Ⓐ   *February 4, 2020*

    Ⓑ   *Dear Principal Sanchez,*

    Ⓒ   *Sincerely,*

    Ⓓ   *Rose Camille*

26   Based on the first paragraph, the author believes that clothing is an important way of being –

    Ⓐ   comfortable

    Ⓑ   focused

    Ⓒ   unique

    Ⓓ   welcoming

27   Which sentence best supports your answer to Question 26?

    Ⓐ   *I think that we should not wear uniforms.*

    Ⓑ   *Every day we have to wear the same clothing, and it is boring.*

    Ⓒ   *I also know my friends want to wear their favorite shirts and jeans.*

    Ⓓ   *We want to express ourselves through our clothing.*

28   Read this sentence from the passage.

> **I will make sure that everything I wear is appropriate for school.**

Which word means about the same as <u>appropriate</u>?

   Ⓐ   beautiful

   Ⓑ   long-lasting

   Ⓒ   similar

   Ⓓ   suitable

29   Read this sentence from the passage.

> **You can still make rules about what we can wear, and we will be sure to respect and follow those rules.**

As it is used in the sentence, what does the word <u>follow</u> mean?

   Ⓐ   enjoy

   Ⓑ   obey

   Ⓒ   shadow

   Ⓓ   understand

30   Which sentence from the passage suggests that not wearing a uniform may help students do better with schoolwork?

Ⓐ   *We also want to be allowed to wear shorts in the warmer weather.*

Ⓑ   *I want to wear clothing that is comfortable so I can focus in school.*

Ⓒ   *In the winter, I want to wear jeans, because my legs are cold when I walk to school.*

Ⓓ   *My mother also says that the uniforms are expensive and she cannot afford to buy me another skirt.*

31   According to the passage, how would not wearing a uniform help parents?

Ⓐ   It would save them money.

Ⓑ   Their children would behave better.

Ⓒ   The parent could pick out the clothing.

Ⓓ   It would make getting ready easier.

32   Select the **two** sentences below in which the author is stating her personal opinion.

☐   *Every day we have to wear the same clothing, and it is boring.*

☐   *The other girls in my class agree with me.*

☐   *They said they don't like their shirts or their pants.*

☐   *I have to wear the same skirt all week and wash it every evening.*

☐   *Overall, I think all the students will be happy if there is no rule about uniforms.*

☐   *We can write new rules about a dress code and you can read them and agree to them.*

33   What is the main purpose of the letter?

    Ⓐ   to inform

    Ⓑ   to instruct

    Ⓒ   to persuade

    Ⓓ   to entertain

34   Describe **two** reasons that the author finds the wool skirt uncomfortable.

1: _____

_____

2: _____

_____

35   How can you tell that the author is still willing to follow rules about what to wear? Use **two** details from the passage to support your answer.

_____

_____

_____

_____

_____

36   Look at the photographs at the end of the passage and read the captions. How do the photographs support the author's main point? Use at least **two** details from the passage in your answer.

_____

_____

_____

_____

_____

_____

_____

_____

_____

_____

_____

_____

_____

_____

_____

End-of-Grade Reading

Practice Test 4

Session 2

Instructions

Read each passage and answer the questions that follow it.

For each multiple-choice question, fill in the circle for the correct answer. For other types of questions, follow the instructions given. Some of the questions require a written answer. Write your answer on the lines provided.

Back in Time

Becky loved going to the museum. It was one of her favorite places. Sometimes Becky's grandmother took her there when she came to visit. There was always plenty to see. Becky's favorite was the room full of beautiful old quilts. Grandma said that they were made from all the old leftovers and worn out pieces of cloth. Each piece had its own story.

"They didn't waste anything in those days," said her grandmother.

Today Becky's grandmother was feeling tired. She stopped to have a rest on a wooden bench in the gallery.

"I'll just have a sit-down and catch you up later," she said.

Becky wandered on looking at more of the displays. She stopped in front of a large colorful quilt. It was made up of lots of tiny triangles stitched together into stars of every color you could imagine. They were all set on a deep blue background.

The lights were kept dim in the room to stop the colors from fading. Maybe that is why Becky began to feel sleepy when she looked at all the patterns. Her eyelids felt heavy and she began to feel a bit dizzy.

In a moment or two, Becky was feeling fine again. She opened her eyes and looked around. But she was not in the museum. She was standing outdoors in the wide open country in the middle of a circle of maybe 20 wagons. There were people all around dressed in old fashioned clothes. They all seemed to be busy. No one seemed to even notice her at first.

It was early evening and the light was beginning to fade. The first stars were appearing in the sky. They seemed so much brighter and clearer than usual.

Becky could smell something cooking and suddenly realized how hungry she was. There was a fire close by and a few of the women were stirring pots and laughing. Becky decided to go over to see what was happening

"Oh, there you are Rebekah! You must be hungry."

There was a small log set down on the ground. The top was smooth and polished and made a perfect seat. One of the women gave her a bowl of stew. It tasted as good as it smelled.

She had finished eating when she heard someone calling her.

It was an old woman sitting not far away. She had a basket at her side and some squares of cloth laid out on her lap.

"Come and sit with me child," she said "My eyes aren't as good as they used to be."
The old woman handed Becky the basket.

"Can you look through those scraps and find another piece like this?"

The old woman was holding a square of faded red cloth. Becky looked through the basket and found some pieces of the red cloth. She gave it to the woman.

"Now this is a bit more tricky," she said pointing to one of the pale green stars on the square on her lap. "I need another piece just like this. There's not so much of it as I remember. It was just an old piece of linen I used to wrap little Georgie in when he was a baby. He loved that old cloth. Even when he got bigger he would clutch it in his little fists as he fell asleep. We all teased him about it later, of course."

"And what about this?" asked Becky holding up some faded yellow calico.

"Oh, I had forgotten about that." A smile came over of the old woman's face. It was hard to tell if whatever she was thinking about made her happy or sad.

"Oh, that was my favorite dress. I wore it to my first grown-up dance. It was yellow like the sunflowers I remembered from home. The first time I danced with your grandpa I was wearing that very dress."

"Are you going to make it into a star?"

"Yes, I'll turn them all into stars."

As the light faded it became harder to sort out the different colors. It was also too dark to sew, although the old lady seemed to do it as much by feel as by sight.

Now it was time to wrap up the evening's work and put it all back into the basket.

"It's time you were going to sleep anyway," said the old woman. "We all have an early start in the morning."

Becky said goodnight. She walked over to the fire and stood for a few minutes watching it. The flickering flames made her sleepy again. She could feel her eyes closing.

Then she heard a familiar voice.

"Oh there you are Becky!" said her grandma. "You must be hungry. Why don't we go to the café and get some cakes. You can tell me all about what you saw."

37   What happens right before Becky travels back in time?

    Ⓐ   She sees a special quilt.

    Ⓑ   She gets dizzy.

    Ⓒ   She has a snack.

    Ⓓ   She trips over.

38   Who is telling the story?

    Ⓐ   a young girl named Becky

    Ⓑ   a museum tour guide

    Ⓒ   a grandmother

    Ⓓ   someone not in the story

39   According to the passage, why are the lights dimmed in the room with the quilts?

    Ⓐ   to create a peaceful atmosphere

    Ⓑ   to help people relax

    Ⓒ   to allow the bright colors to shine

    Ⓓ   to protect the quilts

40   What does each piece of fabric in the quilt the old woman is making represent?

Ⓐ   a dream

Ⓑ   a memory

Ⓒ   a plan

Ⓓ   a regret

41   What does the yellow calico Becky holds up mainly make the old woman think about?

Ⓐ   when one of her children was a baby

Ⓑ   when she first danced with her husband

Ⓒ   when she picked sunflowers in summer

Ⓓ   when she went to school as a girl

42   Read this sentence from the passage.

It was also too dark to sew, although the old lady seemed to do it as much by feel as by sight.

What does this sentence mainly suggest?

Ⓐ   The woman has made many quilts before.

Ⓑ   The woman is rushing to get the quilt finished.

Ⓒ   The woman's hands are starting to ache.

Ⓓ   The woman's sewing skills are quite poor.

43   Which sentence from the third last paragraph contains alliteration?

    Ⓐ   *Becky said goodnight.*

    Ⓑ   *She walked over to the fire and stood for a few minutes watching it.*

    Ⓒ   *The flickering flames made her sleepy again.*

    Ⓓ   *She could feel her eyes closing.*

44   How does Becky help the old woman with the quilt?

    Ⓐ   by creating a design in the shape of a star

    Ⓑ   by sewing the pieces of fabric together

    Ⓒ   by finding the fabric the woman needs

    Ⓓ   by holding up a light so the woman can see

45   In paragraph 7, Becky wakes up and finds she is no longer in the museum. List **two** details that show that she has traveled back in time.

    1: _____

    _____

    2: _____

    _____

46   At the start of the passage, the author states that each piece of cloth "had its own story." How does what the old woman says about the pale green cloth support this idea?

_____

_____

_____

_____

_____

47   Do you think Becky really travels back in time or do you think she has a dream? Explain why you feel that way.

_____

_____

_____

_____

48   What is the main purpose of the passage?

Ⓐ   to teach readers how to make a quilt

Ⓑ   to tell the story behind a special quilt

Ⓒ   to persuade readers to reuse old materials

Ⓓ   to explain why quilts are kept in museums

Volcanoes

A volcano is a mountain that has an opening at the top called a crater. Inside the volcano is molten rock, or magma. Volcanoes are made when magma comes up to the earth's surface from the magma chamber. Once the molten rock is above the earth's surface, it's called lava. When there is too much pressure, volcanoes can explode. When volcanoes erupt, lava shoots out the top. Sometimes, volcanoes can cause mudslides and even other events like tsunamis and earthquakes.

Volcanoes erupt when big pieces of land called tectonic plates move back and forth. The friction between the plates can cause an earthquake or a volcanic eruption. There are three kind of volcanoes. There are active, dormant, and extinct volcanoes. Active volcanoes are the scariest, because they can erupt at any time, and have erupted recently. Dormant volcanoes are like people when they sleep. Dormant volcanoes have not exploded in a long time, but they can always explode again. It can still be dangerous to live near a dormant volcano. Lastly, there are extinct volcanoes. Extinct volcanoes are very old and have not exploded in thousands of years.

There are many famous volcanoes in the world. The Ring of Fire is one place where there are lots of earthquakes and volcanoes. This area is full of active volcanoes. The world's biggest active volcano is Mauna Loa in Hawaii. It is more than 13,500 feet about sea level. One volcano called Mount St. Helens is in Washington State in the Cascade Mountains. Mount St. Helens erupted on May 18, 1980. The eruption killed fifty-seven people and did billions of dollars of damage to land and buildings. The explosion was so loud that people in a few states and even people in Canada heard it.

The Ring of Fire is a chain of volcanoes and earthquakes that border the Pacific Ocean. Almost three quarters of the world's volcanoes occur along this chain.

Even though volcanoes can be very dangerous, there are many places around the world where people can visit volcanoes. Arenal is an active volcano in Costa Rica and is one of the country's most popular tourist attractions. People are able to hike around the base of the volcano, and take photographs of the constant flow of glowing red lava. There are many other volcanoes that people hike near, and even some tours that take people right to the edge of the volcano's crater.

Mount St. Helens is a volcano in the state of Washington. Mount St. Helens erupted in 1980, and caused extensive damage. This photograph shows a steam plume that shot up into the air. The plume reached 3,000 feet!

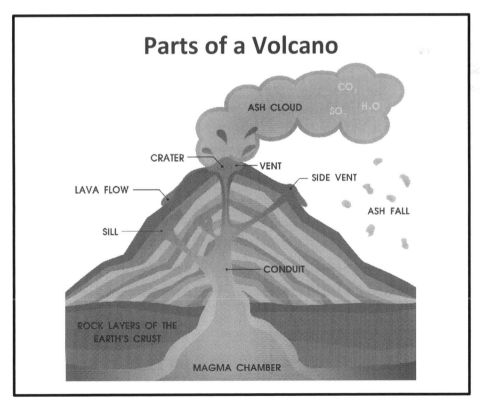

49   Read this sentence from the passage.

When volcanoes erupt, lava shoots out the top.

What does the word <u>shoots</u> mainly emphasize?

Ⓐ   how fast the lava moves

Ⓑ   how loud the eruption is

Ⓒ   how bright the lava glows

Ⓓ   how thick the lava is

50   Which sentence from the first paragraph is best supported by the picture next to the first paragraph?

Ⓐ   *Inside the volcano is molten rock, or magma.*

Ⓑ   *Once the molten rock is above the earth's surface, it's called lava.*

Ⓒ   *When volcanoes erupt, lava shoots out the top.*

Ⓓ   *Sometimes, volcanoes can cause mudslides and even other events like tsunamis and earthquakes.*

51   What is the main difference between active, dormant, and extinct volcanoes?

Ⓐ   how large they are

Ⓑ   when they last erupted

Ⓒ   how they formed

Ⓓ   where they are located

52   According to the passage, where is the world's largest active volcano located?

Ⓐ   Alaska

Ⓑ   California

Ⓒ   Hawaii

Ⓓ   Washington

53   What does the map mainly help readers understand about the Ring of Fire?

Ⓐ   how it formed

Ⓑ   how many volcanoes it has

Ⓒ   where it is located

Ⓓ   why it was given its name

54   Which sentence in the caption of the photograph of Mount St. Helens does the author expect the reader to be most surprised by?

Ⓐ   *Mount St. Helens is a volcano in the state of Washington.*

Ⓑ   *Mount St. Helens erupted in 1980, and caused extensive damage.*

Ⓒ   *This photograph shows a steam plume that shot up into the air.*

Ⓓ   *The plume reached 3,000 feet!*

55 Based on the diagram at the end of the passage, what does the magma pass through to reach the crater?

   Ⓐ   ash cloud

   Ⓑ   conduit

   Ⓒ   side vent

   Ⓓ   sill

56 Circle **all** the terms in the diagram at the end of the passage that are also described in the first paragraph.

ash cloud	ash fall	crater
conduit	lava flow	magma chamber
rock layers	side vent	vent

57 How are magma and lava similar? How are magma and lava different? Use **two** details from the passage in your answer.

_____

_____

_____

_____

58 Describe **two** details given about Mount St. Helens that show that volcanoes can be very dangerous.

1: _____

_____

2: _____

_____

59 Complete the web below by listing **three** other events that can be caused by volcanoes.

Events Caused by Volcanoes

60 The author describes how some volcanoes are tourist attractions. Do you think it is a good idea for people to visit volcanoes? Explain why you feel that way.

_____

_____

_____

_____

_____

Directions: This set has two passages in it. Read each passage and answer the questions that follow it. Then use both passages to answer the final question.

Swinging

Swing, swing, swing,
    Through the drowsy afternoon;
Swing, swing, swing,
    Up I go to meet the moon.
Swing, swing, swing,
    I can see as I go high
    Far along the crimson sky;
    I can see as I come down
    The tops of houses in the town;
    High and low,
    Fast and slow,
    Swing, swing, swing.

Swing, swing, swing,
    See! The sun is gone away;
Swing, swing, swing,
    Gone to make a bright new day.
Swing, swing, swing.
    I can see as up I go
    The poplars waving to and fro,
    I can see as I come down
    The lights are twinkling in the town,
    High and low,
    Fast and slow,
    Swing, swing, swing.

61 Select the **two** lines below that contain alliteration. Tick the box for each line.

☐ Through the drowsy afternoon;

☐ Up I go to meet the moon.

☐ Far along the crimson sky;

☐ Gone to make a bright new day.

☐ The poplars waving to and fro,

☐ The lights are twinkling in the town,

62 In the second line, the speaker describes it as a "drowsy afternoon." This phrase mainly makes the speaker seem –

Ⓐ positive and hopeful

Ⓑ calm and relaxed

Ⓒ brave and daring

Ⓓ curious and puzzled

63 Read this line from the poem.

The poplars waving to and fro,

What does this line help the reader imagine?

Ⓐ what color the poplars are

Ⓑ what the poplars sound like

Ⓒ how the poplars move

Ⓓ why the poplars are important

64 Complete the web below with **three** more words the poet uses to describe how she is moving on the swing.

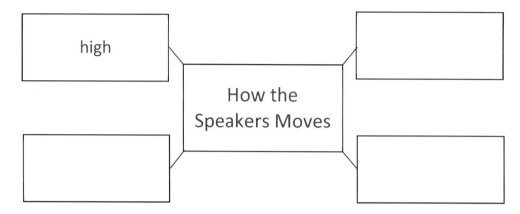

65 Read this line from the poem.

Up I go to meet the moon.

What is the poet exaggerating in this line?

Ⓐ   how great the speaker feels

Ⓑ   how fast the speaker is moving

Ⓒ   how high the speaker is going

Ⓓ   how long the speaker is swinging for

66 How is the setting of the second stanza different from the setting of the first stanza? Use **two** details from the poem to explain your answer.

_____

_____

_____

_____

The Swing
by Robert Louis Stevenson

How do you like to go up in a swing,
Up in the air so blue?
Oh, I do think it the pleasantest thing
Ever a child can do!

Up in the air and over the wall,
Till I can see so wide,
River and trees and cattle and all
Over the countryside –

Till I look down on the garden green,
Down on the roof so brown –
Up in the air I go flying again,
Up in the air and down!

67 Read this line from the poem.

> **Oh, I do think it the pleasantest thing**

What does the word <u>pleasantest</u> mean?

Ⓐ   cheapest

Ⓑ   kindest

Ⓒ   nicest

Ⓓ   simplest

68 Which statement best describes how the first two lines start the poem?

Ⓐ   by asking a question

Ⓑ   by making a statement

Ⓒ   by creating an image

Ⓓ   by giving an opinion

69 How many stanzas does the poem have?

Ⓐ   1

Ⓑ   3

Ⓒ   4

Ⓓ   12

70   Complete the table below by listing **two** more things the speakers sees over the wall and **two** things the speaker sees in the yard.

What the Speaker Sees While Swinging

Over the Wall	In the Yard
1) river	1)
2)	2)
3)	

71   Read this line from the poem.

Up in the air I go flying again,

The word <u>flying</u> suggests that the speaker is moving –

Ⓐ   gently

Ⓑ   oddly

Ⓒ   quickly

Ⓓ   smoothly

72   Circle the phrase from the lines below that is repeated three more times in the poem.

How do you like to go up in a swing,

Up in the air so blue?

Oh, I do think it the pleasantest thing

Ever a child can do!

Directions: Use both passages to answer the following question.

73   The speakers in each poem enjoy swinging for the same reason. Describe what the speakers both enjoy about swinging. Use details from both poems to support your answer.

_____

_____

_____

_____

_____

_____

_____

_____

_____

_____

_____

_____

_____

_____

_____

_____

ANSWER KEY

About North Carolina's Academic Standards

The End-of-Grade ELA/Reading tests assesses a specific set of skills. These skills are described in the *North Carolina Standard Course of Study*. These standards were introduced in 2017 and fully implemented in the 2018-2019 school year.

Student learning is based on these standards throughout the year, and all the questions on the End-of-Grade assessments cover these standards. All the exercises and questions in this book are based on these standards.

Reading Standards

The majority of the questions on the End-of-Grade assessments cover reading standards. The reading standards are divided into the following two areas:

- Reading Standards for Literature
- Reading Standards for Informational Text

Within each of these areas, there are standards that describe specific skills the student should have. The answer key on the following pages summarizes the reading skill assessed by each question.

Scoring Open Response Questions

This practice test book includes open response questions, where students provide a written answer to a question. The answer key gives guidance on how to score these questions. Use the criteria listed as a guide to scoring these questions, and as a guide for giving the student advice on how to improve an answer.

End-of-Grade Reading, Practice Test 1, Session 1

Question	Answer	Reading Skill
1	D	understand, explain, and relate illustrations to a text
2	A	ask and answer questions about a text
3	B	describe characters in a text
4	B	explain how actions contribute to a sequence of events
5	C	describe how parts of texts build on earlier parts
6	snuggled	determine the meaning of words and phrases in a text
7	D	describe characters in a text
8	C	recount or summarize texts
9	C	ask and answer questions about a text
10	4, 2, 1, 3	recount or summarize texts
11	See Below	recount or summarize texts
12	See Below	state a personal point of view
13	See Below	recount or summarize key details
14	C	understand comparison, cause and effect, and sequence
15	C	use text features to locate information
16	B	determine the meaning of words and phrases in a text
17	C	describe the relationship between events, ideas, or concepts
18	D	determine the main idea of a text
19	C	determine the main idea of a text
20	See Below	recount or summarize key details
21	See Below	ask and answer questions about a text
22	See Below	describe the relationship between events, ideas, or concepts
23	See Below	distinguish their own point of view from the author's
24	D	describe the relationship between events, ideas, or concepts
25	B	describe characters in a text
26	C	determine the meaning of words and phrases in a text
27	B	describe characters in a text
28	C	ask and answer questions about a text
29	C	ask and answer questions about a text
30	A	determine the meaning of words and phrases in a text
31	C	recount or summarize texts
32	B	determine and explain a central message, lesson, or moral
33	D	determine and explain a central message, lesson, or moral
34	flew, sprung	determine the meaning of words and phrases in a text
35	See Below	recount or summarize texts
36	See Below	describe characters in a text

Q11.
Give a score of 0, 1, or 2 based on how well the answer meets the criteria listed below.
- It should give a reasonable and accurate description of how Kirsty gets the skunk to leave the cabin.
- The answer should refer to how she opens the window, sits back quietly, and allows the skunk to leave.

Q12.
Give a score of 0, 1, or 2 based on how well the answer meets the criteria listed below.
- It should give an opinion on whether the way Kirsty reacts to the skunk is smart and use relevant supporting details.
- Any opinion can be accepted as long as it is supported, reasonable, and effectively explained.

Q13.
Give a score of 0.5 for each animal correctly listed.
- The correct animals are orangutan, grey wolf, Florida panther, and cougar.

Q20.
Give a score of 1 for each items correctly listed.
- The correct answers are wild flowers, honey, and beeswax.

Q21.
Give a score of 1 for each action correctly listed.
- The correct answers may include building houses on their habitat, riding bikes through their habitat and squashing them, or spreading grass on the bare ground.

Q22.
Give a score of 0, 1, or 2 based on how well the answer meets the criteria listed below.
- It should give a reasonable description of the difference between an endangered and an extinct animal.
- It may refer to how endangered animals have decreased in number, how endangered animals are at risk of becoming extinct, or how extinct animals are gone forever.

Q23.
Give a score of 0, 1, or 2 based on how well the answer meets the criteria listed below.
- It should state that the author would answer that people really need bees.
- It should use relevant supporting details, such as describing how the author explains that bees are needed for pollination.

Q35.
Give a score of 1 for each purpose correctly listed. The correct answers are listed below.
- stings: medicine
- leaves: food or tea
- stalk: stringy bark, linen, or clothing

Q36.
Give a score of 0, 1, 2, 3, or 4 based on how well the answer meets the criteria listed below.
- It should give a reasonable description of how Anna's feelings about nettle change by the end of the play.
- It should show an understanding of the passage and use relevant supporting details.

End-of-Grade Reading, Practice Test 1, Session 2

Question	Answer	Reading Standard
37	B	understand comparison, cause and effect, and sequence
38	B	ask and answer questions about a text
39	black, blue, red, white, yellow	use text features to locate information
40	D	determine the meaning of words and phrases in a text
41	See Below	recount or summarize key details
42	B	determine the main idea of a text
43	C	understand and use information from illustrations
44	A	distinguish their own point of view from the author's
45	D	determine the meaning of words and phrases in a text
46	See Below	ask and answer questions about a text
47	See Below	describe the relationship between events, ideas, or concepts
48	See Below	understand and use information from illustrations
49	B	explain how actions contribute to a sequence of events
50	C	describe characters in a text
51	D	describe characters in a text
52	B	determine the meaning of words and phrases in a text
53	as hard as a bar of iron	understand literal and nonliteral language
54	C	ask and answer questions about a text
55	C	refer to parts of stories, dramas, and poems
56	A	read and comprehend different types of literature
57	A	compare the themes, settings, and plots of texts
58	See Below	describe characters in a text
59	See Below	recount or summarize texts
60	See Below	ask and answer questions about a text
61	A	determine the main idea of a text
62	A	determine the meaning of words and phrases in a text
63	C	describe the connections between sentences and paragraphs
64	D	determine the meaning of words and phrases in a text
65	A	describe the relationship between events, ideas, or concepts
66	See Below	ask and answer questions about a text
67	B	understand comparison, cause and effect, and sequence
68	3rd	describe the relationship between events, ideas, or concepts
69	B	determine the main idea of a text
70	B	use text features to locate information
71	See Below	recount or summarize key details
72	See Below	compare and contrast two texts

Q41.
Give a score of 0.5 for each item correctly listed.
- The correct items are paint thinner, linseed oil, spatula, and palette.

Q46.
Give a score of 1 for each piece of advice correctly listed.
- The correct answers are to not worry about it because you can paint again on top and to stop painting and try again the next day.

Q47.
Give a score of 0, 1, or 2 based on how well the answer meets the criteria listed below.
- It should describe one benefit of choosing acrylic painting over oil painting.
- It should use relevant supporting details from the section titled "What You Will Need."
- It should refer to how you need less materials for acrylic painting.

Q48.
Give a score of 0, 1, or 2 based on how well the answer meets the criteria listed below.
- It should give a reasonable explanation of how the photograph supports the caption.
- It should refer to how it makes painting look fun and relaxing.

Q58.
Give a score of 0, 1, or 2 based on how well the answer meets the criteria listed below.
- It should list the similarity as being that the whale and the elephant are both the largest animals where they live.
- It should list the difference as being that the elephant lives on the land, while the whale lives in the sea.

Q59.
Give a score of 0, 1, or 2 based on how well the answer meets the criteria listed below.
- It should explain how asking both the whale and the elephant to pull the cow out is a trick.
- It should describe how the whale and the elephant are not pulling on a cow, but are pulling against each other.

Q60.
Give a score of 1 for each way correctly listed.
- The correct answers are by forbidding him to eat a blade of grass and by forbidding him to drink a drop of water in the sea.

Q66.
Give a score of 0, 1, or 2 based on how well the answer meets the criteria listed below.
- It should give a reasonable comparison of the uncle's opinion and the brothers' opinion.
- It should refer to how the brothers believe Washington will do well and be promoted, while the uncle believes that he will remain a common sailor.

Q71.
Give a score of 1 for each way correctly listed.
- The correct answers are that he read books and that he observed people he admired.

Q72.

Give a score of 0, 1, 2, 3, or 4 based on how well the answer meets the criteria listed below.

- It should give a reasonable description of how the second passage shows that Washington's life taking a different path would have been a great shame.
- It should show an understanding of the passages and use relevant supporting details from both passages.

End-of-Grade Reading, Practice Test 2, Session 1

Question	Answer	Reading Standard
1	C	ask and answer questions about a text
2	See Below	recount or summarize key details
3	A	ask and answer questions about a text
4	B	distinguish their own point of view from the author's
5	B	use text features to locate information
6	A	determine the meaning of words and phrases in a text
7	C	describe the connections between sentences and paragraphs
8	C	use text features to locate information
9	See Below	recount or summarize key details
10	See Below	ask and answer questions about a text
11	See Below	distinguish their own point of view from the author's
12	See Below	ask and answer questions about a text
13	A	refer to parts of stories, dramas, and poems
14	D	describe characters in a text
15	A	refer to parts of stories, dramas, and poems
16	A	determine the meaning of words and phrases in a text
17	A	ask and answer questions about a text
18	sailing moored sailors	ask and answer questions about a text
19	B	refer to parts of stories, dramas, and poems
20	D	understand literal and nonliteral language
21	D	understand, explain, and relate illustrations to a text
22	A	understand the point of view of narrators or characters
23	See Below	ask and answer questions about a text
24	See Below	describe characters in a text
25	D	ask and answer questions about a text
26	C	understand, explain, and relate illustrations to a text
27	C	explain how actions contribute to a sequence of events
28	A	understand literal and nonliteral language
29	B	understand, explain, and relate illustrations to a text
30	D	describe characters in a text
31	D	determine and explain a central message, lesson, or moral
32	A	determine and explain a central message, lesson, or moral
33	See Below	recount or summarize texts
34	See Below	recount or summarize texts
35	See Below	ask and answer questions about a text
36	See Below	ask and answer questions about a text

Q2.
Give a score of 1 for each column completed correctly. The correct answers are listed below.
- Poor: one common dish
- Average: square wooden plates
- Wealthy: pewter plates, platters, and bowls

Q9.
Give a score of 1 for each correct example.
- The correct answers are maize and rye bread, baked pumpkin with milk, and bean porridge.

Q10.
Give a score of 1 for each problem correctly listed.
- The problems may include that they were thick, that they were clumsy, that they broke easily, or that they had to be melted and moulded again.

Q11.
Give a score of 0, 1, or 2 based on how well the answer meets the criteria listed below.
- It should give an opinion on whether learning at a schoolhouse in colonial times would have been difficult and include supporting details.
- Any opinion can be accepted as long as it is supported, reasonable, and effectively explained.

Q12.
Give a score of 0, 1, or 2 based on how well the answer meets the criteria listed below.
- It should give a reasonable explanation of how the author helps readers imagine the excitement.
- It may refer to how the author describes the windows flying up, the hearty cheers, and the cheers bursting along from house to house.

Q23.
Give a score of 1 for each detail correctly listed.
- The details listed should be that the sofa is mountains and the carpet is sea.

Q24.
Give a score of 0, 1, or 2 based on how well the answer meets the criteria listed below.
- It should make a reasonable inference about how the speaker feels about the town being knocked down.
- The inference should be explained and supported with relevant details.

Q33.
Give a score of 1 for each correct example.
- The correct answers are that he learned how to read there and that he wrote his first short story there.

Q34.
Give a score of 1 for each correct item.
- The correct items, in order, are book, lamp, and table.

Q35.
Give a score of 0, 1, or 2 based on how well the answer meets the criteria listed below.
- It should explain how the library was once a home.
- It should refer to how people lived at the library when a bad storm damaged homes.

Q36.

Give a score of 0, 1, 2, 3, or 4 based on how well the answer meets the criteria listed below.

- It should give a reasonable description of how the outcome of the letter was even better than Thomas expected.
- It should refer to how the library was saved and also made a historical landmark so that it would be there forever.
- It should show an understanding of the passage and use relevant supporting details.

End-of-Grade Reading, Practice Test 2, Session 2

Question	Answer	Reading Standard
37	C	understand, explain, and relate illustrations to a text
38	B	recount or summarize texts
39	B	describe characters in a text
40	B	ask and answer questions about a text
41	A	determine the meaning of words and phrases in a text
42	D	refer to parts of stories, dramas, and poems
43	A	recount or summarize texts
44	See Below	describe characters in a text
45	See Below	describe how parts of texts build on earlier parts
46	See Below	recount or summarize texts
47	See Below	recount or summarize texts
48	See Below	understand the point of view of narrators or characters
49	B	determine the main idea of a text
50	See Below	recount or summarize key details
51	A	describe the relationship between events, ideas, or concepts
52	C	determine the meaning of words and phrases in a text
53	C	describe the relationship between events, ideas, or concepts
54	D	recount or summarize key details
55	C	understand and use information from illustrations
56	B	understand and use information from illustrations
57	See Below	use text features to locate information
58	See Below	use text features to locate information
59	See Below	describe the relationship between events, ideas, or concepts
60	See Below	ask and answer questions about a text
61	A	determine the meaning of words and phrases in a text
62	B	explain how actions contribute to a sequence of events
63	B	determine and explain a central message, lesson, or moral
64	B	describe characters in a text
65	B	ask and answer questions about a text
66	See Below	ask and answer questions about a text
67	B	explain how actions contribute to a sequence of events
68	D	describe characters in a text
69	C	understand, explain, and relate illustrations to a text
70	See Below	recount or summarize texts
71	See Below	ask and answer questions about a text
72	See Below	compare the themes, settings, and plots of texts

Q44.
Give a score of 0, 1, or 2 based on how well the answer meets the criteria listed below.
- It should give a reasonable explanation of what Barry finds funny.
- It should refer to how Barry knows that they are not having liver and onions, but finds it funny to make Tucker think that.

Q45.
Give a score of 0, 1, or 2 based on how well the answer meets the criteria listed below.
- It should give a reasonable explanation of why Barry says they are having "hamburger spaghetti with a house salad."
- It should refer to how Barry is using the three foods his friends like the least.

Q46.
Give a score of 1 for each correct item.
- The correct items, in order, are pudding cup, bookmark, and gel pen.

Q47.
Give a score of 1 for each correct item.
- The correct items, in order, are liver and onions, sushi, and roasted duck and mashed pumpkin.

Q48.
Give a score of 0, 1, or 2 based on how well the answer meets the criteria listed below.
- It should make a reasonable inference about how Barry's friends feel when they see they are having pizza.
- It may describe how they feel excited, happy, or relieved.
- The inference should be explained and supported with relevant details.

Q50.
Give a score of 1 for each correct detail. The correct details are listed below.
- Plants release oxygen into the air.
- Trees release water into the air.

Q57.
Give a score of 0.5 for each box ticked correctly. The correct answers are listed below.
- Temperate Forests: Beech, Oak, Walnut
- Boreal Forests: Fir, Hemlock, Pine

Q58.
Give a score of 1 for each correct definition. The correct answers are listed below.
- Coniferous: trees that have cones
- Deciduous: trees that lose their leaves in fall
- Evergreen: trees that don't lose their leaves

Q59.
Give a score of 0, 1, or 2 based on how well the answer meets the criteria listed below.
- It should make a reasonable comparison of the weather of a tropical forest and a boreal forest.
- The answer may refer to how tropical forests get lots of rain while boreal forests get little or how tropical forests are warm most of the year while boreal forests are mostly cold.

Q60.
Give a score of 1 for each correct similarity. The correct details are listed below.

- They are both temperate rainforests.
- They both run along the coast.
- They are both next to coastal mountains.
- They both get a lot of rain.
- They both have very tall trees.

Q66.
Give a score of 0, 1, or 2 based on how well the answer meets the criteria listed below.

- It should make a reasonable inference about why the snowdrop is the only one.
- It may describe how the snowdrop was the only one strong enough or the only one determined enough to come so early.
- The inference should be explained and supported with relevant details.

Q70.
Give a score of 1 for each row completed correctly. The correct answers are listed below.

- tulips   pink butterflies   They are not red and yellow.
- lily   red and yellow butterflies   They are not pink.

Q71.
Give a score of 0, 1, or 2 based on how well the answer meets the criteria listed below.

- It should give a reasonable description of how the sun rewards the butterflies.
- It should refer to how the sun chased away the rain and shone brightly, or how the sun dried their wings and warmed their bodies.

Q72.
Give a score of 0, 1, 2, 3, or 4 based on how well the answer meets the criteria listed below.

- It should give a reasonable description of how the sun is similar in the two passages.
- It should refer to how the sun helps the snowdrop and helps the butterflies.
- It should show an understanding of the passages and use relevant supporting details from both passages.

End-of-Grade Reading, Practice Test 3, Session 1

Question	Answer	Reading Standard
1	C	refer to parts of stories, dramas, and poems
2	A	understand, explain, and relate illustrations to a text
3	B	ask and answer questions about a text
4	airplane sun	recount or summarize texts
5	D	explain how actions contribute to a sequence of events
6	3rd, 5th	explain how actions contribute to a sequence of events
7	D	determine the meaning of words and phrases in a text
8	C	understand, explain, and relate illustrations to a text
9	A	determine and explain a central message, lesson, or moral
10	See Below	explain how actions contribute to a sequence of events
11	See Below	describe characters in a text
12	See Below	ask and answer questions about a text
13	B	determine the main idea of a text
14	A	determine the meaning of words and phrases in a text
15	C	use text features to locate information
16	D	ask and answer questions about a text
17	A	describe the relationship between events, ideas, or concepts
18	D	distinguish their own point of view from the author's
19	D	use text features to locate information
20	D	determine the meaning of words and phrases in a text
21	See Below	describe the relationship between events, ideas, or concepts
22	See Below	ask and answer questions about a text
23	See Below	recount or summarize key details
24	See Below	ask and answer questions about a text
25	B	refer to parts of stories, dramas, and poems
26	C	understand literal and nonliteral language
27	C	read and comprehend different types of literature
28	A	describe characters in a text
29	See Below	describe characters in a text
30	C	ask and answer questions about a text
31	D	understand literal and nonliteral language
32	A	describe characters in a text
33	B	determine and explain a central message, lesson, or moral
34	See Below	recount or summarize texts
35	See Below	describe how parts of texts build on earlier parts
36	See Below	explain how actions contribute to a sequence of events

Q10.
Give a score of 0, 1, or 2 based on how well the answer meets the criteria listed below.
- It should explain why Harold does black marker outlines.
- It should refer to how he is using the lines Arthur drew with the black marker.

Q11.
Give a score of 1 for each correct detail given.
- The details could include that he asks Arthur why he did it, that he says he would have let Arthur help, that he says it's okay, or that he says he might be able to fix it.

Q12.
Give a score of 0, 1, or 2 based on how well the answer meets the criteria listed below.
- It should make a reasonable inference about why the mother likes the painting so much.
- It may refer to how she likes it because her sons worked on it together.
- The inference should be explained and supported with relevant details.

Q21.
Give a score of 0, 1, or 2 based on how well the answer meets the criteria listed below.
- It should explain why snowkiters are able to travel across flat ground while skiers are not.
- It should refer to how skiers need to travel down a slope to move, while snowkiters can travel across flat ground because they use the wind to make them move.

Q22.
Give a score of 1 for each correct detail given.
- The details could include that you don't need to travel to a snowfield, that you don't need to pay to access a snowfield, that you don't need to pay for ski lifts, or that you can snowkite free in many places.

Q23.
Give a score of 1 for each correct item listed.
- The items listed could include helmet, knee pads, elbow pads, whole body padding, ice claws, jacket, snow pants, gloves, or goggles.

Q24.
Give a score of 0, 1, or 2 based on how well the answer meets the criteria listed below.
- It should explain why lakes are safer than a snowy mountain.
- It may refer to how lakes are nice and smooth or how lakes do not have hidden items like branches or poles.

Q29.
Give a score of 1 for each correct detail given.
- The details could include that he says he is more handsome than the corn, that he says that his flowers are beautiful, that he says it is a pleasure to look at him, or that he suggests there is nothing prettier than he is.

Q34.
Give a score of 1 for each correct detail listed.
- The details listed could include that the trunk is split, that grass and brambles grow out of it, that the tree bends forward, or that the branches hang down to the ground.

Q35.
Give a score of 0, 1, or 2 based on how well the answer meets the criteria listed below.

- It should give a reasonable explanation of why the old willow tree's warning makes the buckwheat more determined to look at the lightning.
- It may refer to how the buckwheat does not like being called inferior or how the buckwheat wants to look into heaven.

Q36.
Give a score of 0, 1, 2, 3, or 4 based on how well the answer meets the criteria listed below.

- It should give a reasonable comparison of how the corn and the buckwheat act during the storm and what happens to each.
- It should refer to how the corn plants bend their heads and fold their leaves to take shelter and are not harmed, and how the buckwheat will not bend its head or take shelter and is burned to blackness by the lightning.
- It should show an understanding of the passage and use relevant supporting details.

End-of-Grade Reading, Practice Test 3, Session 2

Question	Answer	Reading Standard
37	C	understand steps in technical procedures
38	B	understand comparison, cause and effect, and sequence
39	C	ask and answer questions about a text
40	C	determine the main idea of a text
41	C	understand and use information from illustrations
42	B	determine the meaning of words and phrases in a text
43	D	use text features to locate information
44	C	describe the relationship between events, ideas, or concepts
45	C	understand and use information from illustrations
46	See Below	recount or summarize key details
47	See Below	recount or summarize key details
48	See Below	ask and answer questions about a text
49	A	understand, explain, and relate illustrations to a text
50	C	describe how parts of texts build on earlier parts
51	A	determine the meaning of words and phrases in a text
52	D	describe characters in a text
53	C	describe characters in a text
54	B	understand literal and nonliteral language
55	C	ask and answer questions about a text
56	C	ask and answer questions about a text
57	See Below	recount or summarize texts
58	D	refer to parts of stories, dramas, and poems
59	See Below	describe characters in a text
60	See Below	state a personal point of view
61	See Below	recount or summarize key details
62	C	determine the meaning of words and phrases in a text
63	B	ask and answer questions about a text
64	C	understand and use information from illustrations
65	See Below	ask and answer questions about a text
66	See Below	recount or summarize key details
67	B	determine the main idea of a text
68	A	describe the connections between sentences and paragraphs
69	licks its lips yawns	use text features to locate information
70	C	determine the meaning of words and phrases in a text
71	See Below	understand and use information from illustrations
72	See Below	ask and answer questions about a text
73	See Below	compare and contrast two texts

Q46.
Give a score of 1 for each section completed correctly. The correct answers are given below.
- Plants Take In: sunlight, carbon dioxide, water
- Plants Release: oxygen, sugars

Q47.
Give a score of 0.5 for each cell completed correctly. The correct answers are given below.
- Leaf size for plant in bedroom: medium
- Leaf size for plant in full sun: large or largest
- Leaf color for plant in bedroom: light green
- Leaf color for plant in full sun: bright green

Q48.
Give a score of 0, 1, or 2 based on how well the answer meets the criteria listed below.
- It should compare the stems of the plant in the dark closet with the stems of the plant in full sun.
- The stems of the plant in the dark closet should be described as skinny and weak, while the plant in full sun had wide and strong stems.

Q57.
Give a score of 1 for each correct answer.
- The correct answers are where kittens like to sleep, what kittens play with, and what kittens like to eat.

Q59.
Give a score of 0, 1, or 2 based on how well the answer meets the criteria listed below.
- It should make a reasonable inference about how Maria feels when she opens the picnic basket.
- It may describe Maria as feeling excited, overjoyed, or relieved.
- The inference should be explained and supported with relevant details.

Q60.
Give a score of 0, 1, or 2 based on how well the answer meets the criteria listed below.
- It should give an opinion on whether or not Maria will take good care of the kitten.
- Any opinion can be accepted as long as it is supported, reasonable, and effectively explained.

Q61.
Give a score of 1 for each correct answer.
- The correct answers are breakable items, dangerous chemicals, cleaning products.

Q65.
Give a score of 0, 1, or 2 based on how well the answer meets the criteria listed below.
- It should explain how toys can stop puppies from doing damage.
- It should refer to how puppies do damage when they are bored and how toys stop puppies from becoming bored.

Q66.
Give a score of 1 for each problem correctly described.
- The correct problems include that you could lose the puppy, that the puppy could run onto the road, or that the puppy could be harmed by a larger dog.

Q71.

Give a score of 1 for each detail correctly described.

- The correct details include that the dog is cowering, that the dog is shaking or trembling, that the dog is snarling, or that the dog is baring its teeth.

Q72.

Give a score of 0, 1, or 2 based on how well the answer meets the criteria listed below.

- It should give a reasonable explanation of why it is important to tell that a dog is very stressed.
- It may refer to how dogs that are stressed may start barking or biting, and how knowing that a dog is stressed allows you to take action to calm it.

Q73.

Give a score of 0, 1, 2, 3, or 4 based on how well the answer meets the criteria listed below.

- It should give a reasonable description of how the information in "The Body Language of Dogs" would help someone play with a puppy in a suitable way.
- It should relate the information about the body language of dogs to a puppy becoming stressed during play.
- It should show an understanding of the passages and use relevant supporting details from both passages.

End-of-Grade Reading, Practice Test 4, Session 1

Question	Answer	Reading Standard
1	D	determine the meaning of words and phrases in a text
2	A	determine the main idea of a text
3	C	understand and use information from illustrations
4	B	understand and use information from illustrations
5	3, 5	ask and answer questions about a text
6	Three Sisters	understand and use information from illustrations
7	A	use text features to locate information
8	D	distinguish their own point of view from the author's
9	See Below	recount or summarize key details
10	See Below	describe the relationship between events, ideas, or concepts
11	See Below	describe the relationship between events, ideas, or concepts
12	See Below	distinguish their own point of view from the author's
13	D	refer to parts of stories, dramas, and poems
14	B	ask and answer questions about a text
15	C	refer to parts of stories, dramas, and poems
16	B	describe characters in a text
17	last	describe characters in a text
18	C	refer to parts of stories, dramas, and poems
19	A	describe how parts of texts build on earlier parts
20	B	understand, explain, and relate illustrations to a text
21	See Below	describe characters in a text
22	See Below	recount or summarize texts
23	See Below	understand the point of view of narrators or characters
24	See Below	ask and answer questions about a text
25	B	use text features to locate information
26	C	distinguish their own point of view from the author's
27	D	distinguish their own point of view from the author's
28	D	determine the meaning of words and phrases in a text
29	B	determine the meaning of words and phrases in a text
30	B	recount or summarize key details
31	A	ask and answer questions about a text
32	1st, 5th	distinguish their own point of view from the author's
33	C	determine the main idea of a text
34	See Below	recount or summarize key details
35	See Below	ask and answer questions about a text
36	See Below	understand and use information from illustrations

Q9.
Give a score of 1 for each correct activity listed.
- The correct answers include photography, sightseeing, hiking, and stargazing.

Q10.
Give a score of 1 for each difference correctly described. Possible answers are listed below.
- The Wildcat Trail is 4 miles, while the Valley Drive is 17 miles.
- The Wildcat Trail is a walking tour, while Valley Drive is by car.
- The Wildcat Trail allows people to walk, while leaving the trail is not allowed on Valley Drive.

Q11.
Give a score of 0, 1, or 2 based on how well the answer meets the criteria listed below.
- It should give a reasonable comparison of the activities at Mexican Hut and Monument Valley.
- It may refer to how they both offer tours or how they both offer outdoor activities like rock climbing.

Q12.
Give a score of 0, 1, or 2 based on how well the answer meets the criteria listed below.
- It should give an opinion on whether or not Monument Valley sounds like a magical place.
- Any opinion can be accepted as long as it is supported, reasonable, and effectively explained.

Q21.
Give a score of 0, 1, or 2 based on how well the answer meets the criteria listed below.
- It should explain that the other children do not care about the water on the sand.
- It should provide supporting details such as describing how the children ignore Peter's concerns or how they do not wait for Peter but go home instead.

Q22.
Give a score of 1 for each correct reason listed.
- The correct answers are that he cannot find any stones and that going to tell the people would take too long.

Q23.
Give a score of 0, 1, or 2 based on how well the answer meets the criteria listed below.
- It should give an opinion on whether Peter's mother would still be mad at the end of the play.
- It should refer to how she thought he was being naughty and staying away, but then learns that he was saving the town.
- Any opinion can be accepted as long as it is supported, reasonable, and effectively explained.

Q24.
Give a score of 1 for each correct way listed.
- The correct answers include that soldiers carry him on their shoulders, that people cheer for him, and that the king is going to thank him.

Q34.
Give a score of 1 for each correct reason listed.
- The correct reasons are that the skirt is itchy and that the skirt slides around her stomach.

Q35.
Give a score of 0, 1, or 2 based on how well the answer meets the criteria listed below.
- It should give a reasonable explanation of how you can tell that the author will follow rules about what to wear.
- It may refer to how the author says that the principal can still make rules about what to wear or how the author suggests writing a dress code.

Q36.
Give a score of 0, 1, 2, 3, or 4 based on how well the answer meets the criteria listed below.
- It should give a reasonable description of how the photographs and captions support the author's main point.
- It should show an understanding of the passage and use relevant supporting details.

End-of-Grade Reading, Practice Test 4, Session 2

Question	Answer	Reading Standard
37	B	describe how parts of texts build on earlier parts
38	D	understand the point of view of narrators or characters
39	D	ask and answer questions about a text
40	B	recount or summarize texts
41	B	ask and answer questions about a text
42	A	describe characters in a text
43	C	understand literal and nonliteral language
44	C	recount or summarize texts
45	See Below	ask and answer questions about a text
46	See Below	describe how parts of texts build on earlier parts
47	See Below	read and comprehend different types of literature
48	B	read and comprehend different types of literature
49	A	determine the meaning of words and phrases in a text
50	C	understand and use information from illustrations
51	B	describe the relationship between events, ideas, or concepts
52	C	use text features to locate information
53	C	understand and use information from illustrations
54	D	describe the connections between sentences and paragraphs
55	B	understand and use information from illustrations
56	crater magma chamber	understand and use information from illustrations
57	See Below	ask and answer questions about a text
58	See Below	recount or summarize key details
59	See Below	recount or summarize key details
60	See Below	distinguish their own point of view from the author's
61	2nd, 6th	understand literal and nonliteral language
62	B	describe characters in a text
63	C	ask and answer questions about a text
64	See Below	ask and answer questions about a text
65	C	understand literal and nonliteral language
66	See Below	refer to parts of stories, dramas, and poems
67	C	determine the meaning of words and phrases in a text
68	A	refer to parts of stories, dramas, and poems
69	B	refer to parts of stories, dramas, and poems
70	See Below	recount or summarize texts
71	C	understand literal and nonliteral language
72	Up in the air	refer to parts of stories, dramas, and poems
73	See Below	compare the themes, settings, and plots of texts

Q45.
Give a score of 1 for each correct detail listed.
- The correct details are that there are wagons and that people are dressed in old fashioned clothing.

Q46.
Give a score of 0, 1, or 2 based on how well the answer meets the criteria listed below.
- It should explain how the information about the pale green cloth supports the idea that each cloth has its own story.
- It should refer to how the pale green cloth was from linen she wrapped her child in as a baby.

Q47.
Give a score of 0, 1, or 2 based on how well the answer meets the criteria listed below.
- It should give an opinion on whether Becky really traveled back in time or had a dream.
- Any opinion can be accepted as long as it is supported, reasonable, and effectively explained.

Q57.
Give a score of 1 for a correct similarity and 1 for a correct difference.
- The similarity should be that they are both molten rock.
- The difference should be that magma is below the surface and lava is above the surface.

Q58.
Give a score of 1 for each correct detail listed.
- The correct details include that the volcano killed fifty-seven people, did billions of dollars of damage, or was so loud that it was heard from several states away and in Canada.

Q59.
Give a score of 1 for each correct event listed.
- The correct events are mudslide, tsunami, and earthquake.

Q60.
Give a score of 0, 1, or 2 based on how well the answer meets the criteria listed below.
- It should give an opinion on whether or not it is a good idea for people to visit volcanoes.
- Any opinion can be accepted as long as it is supported, reasonable, and effectively explained.

Q64.
Give a score of 1 for each correct word listed.
- The correct words include down, low, fast, and slow.

Q66.
Give a score of 0, 1, or 2 based on how well the answer meets the criteria listed below.
- It should compare the settings of the first and second stanzas.
- It should refer to how it is later in day in the second stanza or afternoon in the first stanza and evening in the second stanza.
- It may refer to how the sun has set or how the lights are on in the town.

Q70.
Give a score of 0.5 for each correct thing seen listed. The correct answers are listed below.
- Over the Wall: trees, cattle, countryside
- In the Yard: garden, roof

Q73.

Give a score of 0, 1, 2, 3, or 4 based on how well the answer meets the criteria listed below.

- It should give a reasonable description of what both speakers enjoy about swinging.
- It should show an understanding of the passages and use relevant supporting details from both passages.

Made in the USA
Columbia, SC
11 March 2022

57530278R00117